Writing Conversational Korean For Beginners by Chelsea Guerra, Katarina Pollock, and Yujin Kim

Published by Gooseapple Books, LLC
209 Archer Street
Houston, TX, 77009
www.gooseapplebooks.com

Cover by Yujin Kim
Edited by Yujin Kim
Illustrations from pngtree.com

ISBN: 978-1-7376777-7-2 (print)

First Edition

GOOSE APPLE
BOOKS

We would like
to thank our testers:
Renee, Jane, Sarah, and Rebeca.
We also would like to thank Lacey and Russell for all
of their input and encouragement.

목차 | Table of Contents

목차 | Table of Contents

 **활용법**

How to Use This Book

WHAT IS THIS BOOK?

This book is designed to help beginner learners develop their Korean writing skills. The contents are organized around 24 different writing prompts, which aim to get you talking about topics that are related to your own life. Each of the 24 chapters follows the same 10 page structure [see next 5 pages].

WHAT DO I NEED TO USE THIS BOOK?

This book is not designed for absolute beginners. In order to use this book most effectively learners will need knowledge of the Korean alphabet and some basic grammar structures. Use this book as a place to practice your existing beginner skills and develop more confidence in your sentence building abilities.

WHERE DO I GO AFTER THIS BOOK?

Our original writing prompt series (*Writing Conversational Korean*) was created as a resource for intermediate and advanced students. However, many beginner level learners interested in using the series expressed a need for a beginner-friendly book to prepare them for the intermediate series. This is that book. After completing this book we hope you feel confident to pursue the *Writing Conversational Korean* series as your next step in developing your writing skills.

WHO ARE THE AUTHORS?

The Gooseapple Books team is made up of three people; Chelsea, Katarina, and Yujin. Chelsea and Katarina are longtime Korean learners who provide the Korean learner perspective, while Yujin brings the native speaker perspective. Together we've endeavored to create a fun and unique way to practice writing that builds confidence and familiarity with the language. Thank you for your purchase, and we hope you enjoy practicing with *Writing Conversational Korean for Beginners*.

More Books
From Gooseapple Books

Writing Conversation-al Korean: Book One

" 코를 골아요?"
and 200 other
writing prompts

Writing Conversation-al Korean: Book Two

"영화를 보면서 울어 본 적이 있어요?"
and 200 other
writing prompts

1000 Korean Prompts
For Writing & Speaking

Conversational Korean Grammar
A grammar resource for beginners

For more information, check out the books on our website: www.gooseapplebooks.com

(1) Question Page

The aim of this page is to introduce the prompt.

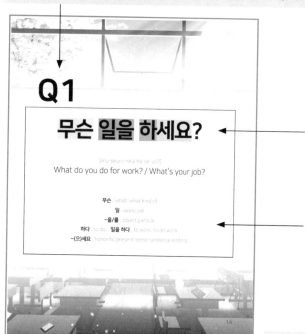

Here is the main question for this chapter. The parts of the question are color coded to help you identify them. Below the question is the pronunciation, and the English translation of the question.

Here is a breakdown of the main question above, listing all vocabulary words and grammar conjugations.

(2) 대답 (Answer) Page

The aim of this page is to show an example answer.

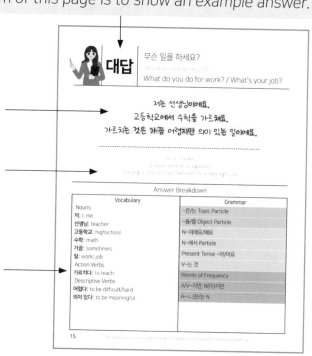

Here is an example answer to this chapter's main question. Grammar points are color coded and correspond to the breakdown below.

Here is an English translation.

Here is a breakdown of the vocabulary and grammar in the example answer. The grammar list corresponds to the chapters in *Conversational Korean Grammar,* but you can also easily look these forms up online.

How to Use This Book

(3) 설명 (Explanation) Page

The aim of this page is to break down a sentence in more detail.

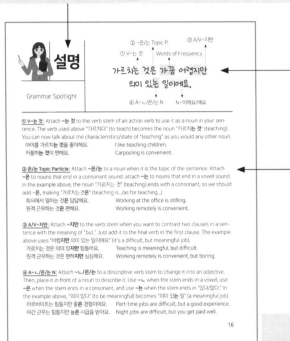

This area shows one sentence from the example answer. Each grammar form present in this sentence is highlighted and labeled.

This area shows further explanation for some of the grammar forms appearing in the sentence above, while also providing more examples of each grammar form in use.

(4) 문법 (Grammar) Page

The aim of this page is to practice Korean grammar.

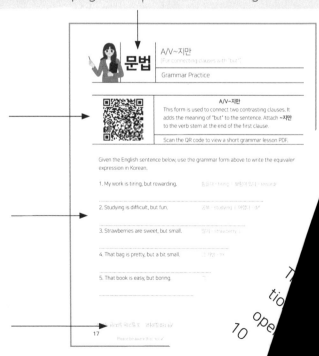

Here you can scan the QR code to download a short explanation of the grammar form. This information is pulled from our book *Conversational Korean Grammar*.

In this section you can solve practice problems to test your understanding of the grammar form.

The answers are upside down at the bottom of the page.

(5) 어휘 (Vocabulary) Page

The aim of this page is to support your vocabulary.

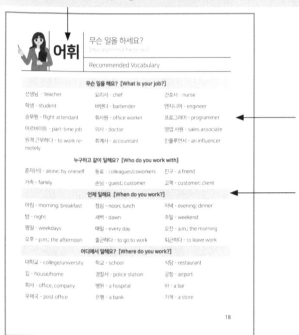

This page gives you vocabulary that you can use when answering the Extended Question section on the next two pages.

The title for each group of vocabulary words matches the Extended Question boxes on the next two pages. You can use these words to help you make your own answers.

(6) & (7) 육하원칙 (Extending the Question) Page

The aim of these pages is to get you to develop & extend your answer.

On these pages 4 questions relating to the main question of this chapter are provided. Answering these questions will help you build your answer to the main question.

Each question has 5 example answers using various grammar forms and vocabulary. English translations are also provided.

Try writing your own answer to each question on the lines below. These questions are open ended; there are no right answers.

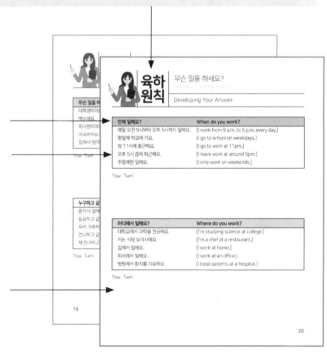

(8) 쓰기 (Writing) Page

The aim of this page is to get you to practice your writing skills.

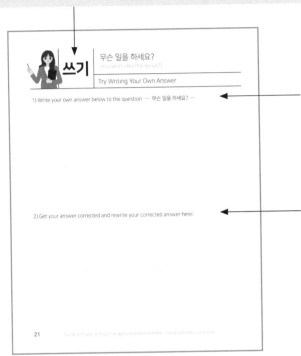

This is the space for you to write your answer to the main question for this chapter.

We encourage you to either consult with a native speaker (a friend, tutor, etc.), or upload your answer to a website for corrections. Once you've gotten feedback, use this space to rewrite your corrected answer and any notes you have about the changes made.

GETTING CORRECTIONS ON YOUR WRITING:

We strongly recommend that you get your writing checked by native speakers. You can ask a Korean teacher or tutor to check your writing, or you can use one of these apps/websites to get your writing checked for free:

1. HelloTalk	2. HiNative	3. r/WriteStreakKorean

(9) 대화 (Conversation) Page

The aim of this page is to practice your reading & comprehension skills.

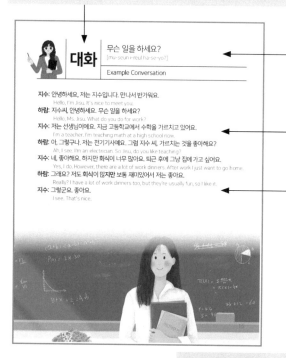

대화   무슨 일을 하세요?
[mu-seun i-reul ha-se-yo?]

Example Conversation

지수: 안녕하세요. 저는 지수입니다. 만나서 반가워요.
    Hello, I'm Jisu. It's nice to meet you.
하람: 지수씨, 안녕하세요. 무슨 일을 하세요?
    Hello, Ms. Jisu. What do you do for work?
지수: 저는 선생님이에요. 지금 고등학교에서 수학을 가르치고 있어요.
    I'm a teacher. I'm teaching math at a high school now.
하람: 아, 그렇구나. 저는 전기기사예요. 그럼 지수 씨, 가르치는 것을 좋아해요?
    Ah, I see. I'm an electrician. So Jisu, do you like teaching?
지수: 네, 좋아해요. 하지만 회식이 너무 많아요. 퇴근 후에 그냥 집에 가고 싶어요.
    Yes, I do. However, there are a lot of work dinners. After work I just want to go home.
하람: 그래요? 저도 회식이 많지만 보통 재미있어서 저는 좋아요.
    Really? I have a lot of work dinners too, but they're usually fun, so I like it.
지수: 그렇군요. 좋아요.
    I see. That's nice.

This page shows a simple, yet natural conversation about the topic.

The grammar point from the 문법 (Grammar) Page appears bolded in the conversation.

The topic from the following 문화 (Culture Note) Page appears highlighted in the conversation.

(10) 문화 (Culture Note) Page

The aim of this page is to tell you about Korean society & culture.

The final page in each chapter gives insight into a cultural point related to the main question of the chapter. The Korean term on this page also appears highlighted in the conversation on the previous 대화 (Conversation) Page.

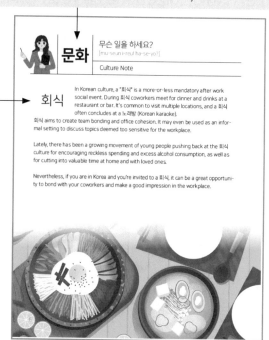

문화   무슨 일을 하세요?
[mu-seun i-reul ha-se-yo?]

Culture Note

회식   In Korean culture, a "회식" is a more-or-less mandatory after work social event. During 회식 coworkers meet for dinner and drinks at a restaurant or bar. It's common to visit multiple locations, and a 회식 often concludes at a 노래방 (Korean karaoke).

회식 aims to create team bonding and office cohesion. It may even be used as an informal setting to discuss topics deemed too sensitive for the workplace.

Lately, there has been a growing movement of young people pushing back at the 회식 culture for encouraging reckless spending and excess alcohol consumption, as well as for cutting into valuable time at home and with loved ones.

Nevertheless, if you are in Korea and you're invited to a 회식, it can be a great opportunity to bond with your coworkers and make a good impression in the workplace.

Q1

무슨 일을 하세요?

[mu-seun i-reul ha-se-yo?]

What do you do for work? / What's your job?

무슨 : what; what kind of

일 : work; job

~을/를 : object particle

하다 : to do;　일을 하다 : to work; to do work

~(으)세요 : honorific present tense sentence ending

대답

무슨 일을 하세요?

[mu-seun i-reul ha-se-yo?]

What do you do for work? / What's your job?

저는 선생님이에요.

고등학교에서 수학을 가르쳐요.

가르치는 것은 가끔 어렵지만 의미 있는 일이에요.

I'm a teacher.
I teach math at a highschool.
Teaching is difficult sometimes, but it's a meaningful job.

Answer Breakdown

Vocabulary	Grammar
Nouns	~은/는 Topic Particle
저: I; me	~을/를 Object Particle
선생님: a teacher	N~이에요/예요
고등학교: a high school	N~에서 Particle
수학: math	Present Tense ~아/어요
가끔: sometimes	V~는 것
일: work; job	Words of Frequency
Action Verbs	A/V~지만, N(이)지만
가르치다: to teach	A~ㄴ/은/는 N
Descriptive Verbs	
어렵다: to be difficult/hard	
의미 있다: to be meaningful	

설명

Grammar Spotlight

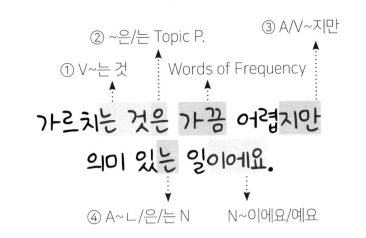

② ~은/는 Topic P.

③ A/V~지만

① V~는 것   Words of Frequency

가르치는 것은 가끔 어렵지만
의미 있는 일이에요.

④ A~ㄴ/은/는 N   N~이에요/예요

① V~는 것: Attach **~는 것** to the verb stem of an action verb to use it as a noun in your sentence. The verb used above "가르치다" (to teach) becomes the noun "가르치**는 것**" (teaching). You can now talk about the characteristics/state of "teaching" as you would any other noun.

아이를 가르치**는 것**을 좋아해요.	I like teaching children.
카풀하**는 것**이 편해요.	Carpooling is convenient.

② 은/는 Topic Particle: Attach **~은/는** to a noun when it is the topic of the sentence. Attach **~은** to nouns that end in a consonant sound; attach **~는** to nouns that end in a vowel sound. In the example above, the noun "가르치는 것" (teaching) ends with a consonant, so we should add **~은**, making "가르치는것**은**" (teaching is.../as for teaching...)

회사에서 일하는 것**은** 답답해요.	Working at the office is stifling.
원격 근무하는 것**은** 편해요.	Working remotely is convenient.

③ A/V~지만: Attach **~지만** to the verb stem when you want to contrast two clauses in a sentence with the meaning of "but." Just add it to the final verb in the first clause. The example above uses "어렵**지만** 의미 있는 일이에요" (it's a difficult, but meaningful job).

가르치는 것은 의미 있**지만** 힘들어요.	Teaching is meaningful, but difficult.
원격 근무하는 것은 편하**지만** 심심해요.	Working remotely is convenient, but boring.

④ A~ㄴ/은/는 N: Attach **~ㄴ/은/는** to a descriptive verb stem to change it into an adjective. Then, place it in front of a noun to describe it. Use **~ㄴ** when the stem ends in a vowel, use **~은** when the stem ends in a consonant, and use **~는** when the stem ends in "있다/없다." In the example above, "의미 있다" (to be meaningful) becomes "의미 있**는** 일" (a meaningful job).

아르바이트는 힘들지만 좋**은** 경험이에요.	Part-time jobs are difficult, but a good experience.
야간 근무는 힘들지만 높**은** 시급을 받아요.	Night jobs are difficult, but you get paid well.

문법

A/V~지만
[For connecting clauses with "but"]

Grammar Practice

A/V~지만

This form is used to connect two contrasting clauses. It adds the meaning of "but" to the sentence. Attach **~지만** to the verb stem at the end of the first clause.

Scan the QR code to view a short grammar lesson PDF.

Given the English sentence below, use the grammar form above to write the equivalent expression in Korean.

1. My work is tiring, but rewarding.

힘들다 - tiring | 보람이 있다 - rewarding

....

2. Studying is difficult, but fun.

공부 - studying | 어렵다 - difficult | 재미있다 - fun

....

3. Strawberries are sweet, but small.

딸기 - strawberry | 달다 - sweet | 작다 - small

....

4. That bag is pretty, but a bit small.

그 가방 - that bag | 예쁘다 - pretty | 조금 - a bit

....

5. That book is easy, but boring.

그 책 - that book | 쉽다 - easy | 지루하다 - boring

....

Please be aware that not all sentences have one exact translation, so answers may vary slightly.

어휘

무슨 일을 하세요?
[mu-seun i-reul ha-se-yo?]

Recommended Vocabulary

무슨 일을 해요? [What is your job?]

선생님 - a teacher

요리사 - a chef

간호사 - a nurse

학생 - a student

바텐더 - a bartender

엔지니어 - an engineer

승무원 - a flight attendant

회사원 - an office worker

프로그래머 - a programmer

아르바이트 - a part-time job

의사 - a doctor

영업 사원 - a sales associate

원격 근무하다 - to work remotely

회계사 - an accountant

인플루언서 - an influencer

누구하고 같이 일해요? [Who do you work with]

혼자(서) - alone; by oneself

동료 - a colleague/coworker

친구 - a friend

가족 - family

손님 - a guest/customer

고객 - a customer/client

언제 일해요 [When do you work?]

아침 - morning; breakfast

점심 - noon; lunch

저녁 - evening; dinner

밤 - night

새벽 - dawn

주말 - weekend

평일 - weekdays

매일 - every day

오전 - a.m.; the morning

오후 - p.m.; the afternoon

출근하다 - to go to work

퇴근하다 - to leave work

어디에서 일해요? [Where do you work?]

대학교 - a college/university

학교 - a school

식당 - a restaurant

집 - house/home

경찰서 - a police station

공항 - an airport

회사 - an office/company

병원 - a hospital

바 - a bar

우체국 - a post office

은행 - a bank

가게 - a store

무슨 일을 하세요?
[mu-seun i-reul ha-se-yo?]

Developing Your Answer

무슨 일을 해요?	What is your job?
대학생이에요.	[I'm a college student.]
백수예요.	[I'm unemployed.]
회사원이에요.	[I'm an office worker.]
아르바이트생이에요.	[I work part time.]
집에서 원격 근무해요.	[I work remotely from home.]

Your Turn:

누구하고 같이 일해요?	Who do you work with?
혼자서 일해요.	[I work alone.]
동료하고 같이 일해요.	[I work with colleagues.]
우리 가족하고 같이 일해요.	[I work with my family.]
언니하고 같이 일해요.	[I work with my older sister.]
제 친구하고 같이 일해요.	[I work with my friends.]

Your Turn:

육하원칙

무슨 일을 하세요?
[mu-seun i-reul ha-se-yo?]

Developing Your Answer

언제 일해요?	When do you work?
매일 오전 9시부터 오후 5시까지 일해요.	[I work from 9 a.m. to 5 p.m. every day.]
평일에 학교에 가요.	[I go to school on weekdays.]
밤 11시에 출근해요.	[I go to work at 11pm.]
오후 5시 쯤에 퇴근해요.	[I leave work at around 5pm.]
주말에만 일해요.	[I only work on weekends.]

Your Turn:

....

....

어디에서 일해요?	Where do you work?
대학교에서 과학을 전공해요.	[I'm studying science at college.]
저는 식당 요리사예요.	[I'm a chef at a restaurant.]
집에서 일해요.	[I work at home.]
회사에서 일해요.	[I work at an office.]
병원에서 환자를 치료해요.	[I treat patients at a hospital.]

Your Turn:

....

....

....

19

1) Write your own answer below to the question -- 무슨 일을 하세요? --

2) Get your answer corrected and rewrite your corrected answer here:

You can post your writing on an app/website like *Hellotalk* or *Hinative* for free corrections.

대화

무슨 일을 하세요?
[mu-seun i-reul ha-se-yo?]

Example Conversation

지수: 안녕하세요, 저는 지수입니다. 만나서 반가워요.
Hello, I'm Jisu. It's nice to meet you.

하람: 지수씨, 안녕하세요. 무슨 일을 하세요?
Hello, Jisu. What do you do for work?

지수: 저는 선생님이에요. 지금 고등학교에서 수학을 가르치고 있어요.
I'm a teacher. I'm teaching math at a high school now.

하람: 아, 그렇구나. 저는 전기기사예요. 그럼 지수 씨, 가르치는 것을 좋아해요?
Ah, I see. I'm an electrician. So Jisu, do you like teaching?

지수: 네, 좋아해요. 하지만 회식이 너무 많아요. 퇴근 후에 그냥 집에 가고 싶어요.
Yes, I do. However, there are a lot of work dinners. After work I just want to go home.

하람: 그래요? 저도 회식이 많**지만** 보통 재미있어서 저는 좋아요.
Really? I have a lot of work dinners too, but they're usually fun, so I like it.

지수: 그렇군요. 좋아요.
I see. That's nice.

회식

In Korean culture, a "회식" is a more-or-less mandatory after work social event. During a 회식, coworkers meet for dinner and drinks at a restaurant or bar. It's common to visit multiple locations, and a 회식 often concludes at a 노래방 (Korean karaoke).

A 회식 aims to create team bonding and office cohesion. It may even be used as an informal setting to discuss topics deemed too sensitive for the workplace.

Lately, there has been a growing movement of young people pushing back against the 회식 culture for encouraging reckless spending and excess alcohol consumption, as well as for cutting into valuable time at home and with loved ones.

Nevertheless, if you are in Korea and you're invited to a 회식, it can be a great opportunity to bond with your coworkers and make a good impression in the workplace.

어떤 계절을 가장 좋아하세요?

[eo-tteon gye-jeo-reul ga-jang jo-a-ha-se-yo?]

What's your favorite season?

어떤: what; what kind of; which

계절 : season

~을/를 : object particle

가장 : the most/best

좋아하다 : to like

~(으)세요 : honorific present tense sentence ending

대답

어떤 계절을 가장 좋아하세요?
[eo-tteon gye-jeo-reul ga-jang jo-a-ha-se-yo?]
What's your favorite season?

제가 가장 좋아하는 계절은 가을이에요.

가을은 너무 덥지 않고 너무 춥지 않아서 좋아해요.

그리고 가을에는 단풍을 즐길 수 있어요.

My favorite season is fall.
I like fall because it isn't too hot, and it isn't too cold.
And in fall I can enjoy the fall colors.

Answer Breakdown

Vocabulary	Grammar
Nouns	~이/가 Subject Particle
제 - my	~은/는 Topic Particle
가장 - most; best	~을/를 Object Particle
계절 - season	N~이에요/예요
가을 - autumn; fall	A/V~지 않다
너무 - really; very; so; too much	Present Tense ~아/어요
그리고 - And (sentence starter)	~에 Time Particle
단풍 - the fall leaves/colors	A/V~고
Action Verbs	A/V~아/어서
좋아하다 - to like	그리고, 그래서 & 하지만
즐기다 - to enjoy	가장 & 제일
Descriptive Verbs	V~는 N
덥다 - to be hot	V~ㄹ/을 수 있다/없다
춥다 - to be cold	

The grammar is color-coded to match chapters in *Conversational Korean Grammar*.

설명

Grammar Spotlight

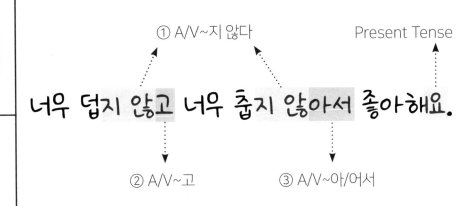

① A/V~지 않다

② A/V~고

③ A/V~아/어서

Present Tense

너무 덥지 않고 너무 춥지 않아서 좋아해요.

① A/V~지 않다: When attached to the verb stem of either a descriptive verb or an action verb, **~지 않다** negates that verb with the meaning of "doesn't" or "isn't." In the example above, the verb "덥다"(to be hot) becomes "덥**지 않다**" (to not be hot).

가을은 덥**지 않아요**.   Fall isn't hot.

여름은 춥**지 않아요**.   Summer isn't cold.

② A/V~고: The form **~고** attaches to the verb stem, and is used to connect two clauses in a sentence together with the meaning "and". Just attach **~고** to the final verb in the first clause. The sentence above shows clause 1: "너무 덥지 않다" (to not be too hot), and clause 2: "너무 춥지 않다" (to not be too cold). **~고** attaches to the clause 1 verb stem "덥지 않-" joining the two clauses together to make "너무 덥지 않**고** 너무 춥지 않아요" (it isn't too hot and it isn't too cold).

겨울에는 습하지 않**고** 건조해요.   In winter it's not humid and it's dry.

가을은 많이 덥지 않**고** 선선해요.   Autumn isn't very hot and it feels cool.

③ A/V~아/어서: The form **~아/어서** attaches to a verb stem to connect two clauses. It is used when clause 1 of a sentence is the reason that clause 2 happens, and it can mean "so/since/because." To connect the two clauses, just attach **~아/어서** to the final verb of the first clause. The sentence above shows clause 1: "너무 춥지 않다" (it's not too cold), and clause 2: "좋아하다" (to like it). **~아/어서** attaches to the verb stem "춥지 않-" in clause 1, becoming "너무 춥지 않**아서** 좋아해요" (I like it because it isn't too cold).

가을은 많이 춥지 않**아서** 좋아해요.   I like autumn because it isn't too cold.

봄에는 꽃이 많이 피고 따뜻**해서** 좋아해요.   I like spring because there are lots of flowers and it's warm.

문법

A/V~지 않다
[For negating verbs]

Grammar Practice

A/V~지 않다
This form is used to negate a verb/make a negative sentence. Attach **~지 않다** to a verb stem to give the meaning of "(subject) doesn't/isn't."

Scan the QR code to view a short grammar lesson PDF.

Given the English sentence below, use the grammar form above to write the equivalent expression in Korean.

1. I don't go see the fall colors in the fall.   가을 - fall | 단풍 구경을 가다 - go see the fall colors

....

2. I don't like summer.   여름 - summer | 좋아하다 - to like

....

3. I don't swim in the spring.   봄 - spring | 수영하다 - to swim

....

4. I don't eat icecream in the winter.   겨울 - winter | 아이스크림 - icecream | 먹다 - eat

....

5. It doesn't snow here in the winter.   여기 - here | 눈이 오다 - to snow

....

Please be aware that not all sentences have one exact translation, so answers may vary slightly.

어휘

어떤 계절을 가장 좋아하세요?
[eo-tteon gye-jeo-reul ga-jang jo-a-ha-se-yo?]

Recommended Vocabulary

뭘 할 수 있어요? [What can you do?]

수영하다 - to swim

눈사람 - a snowman

핫초코 - hot chocolate

단풍 - the fall colors

벚꽃 - cherry blossoms

구경하다 - to view/spectate

수박 - a watermelon

따뜻한 옷 - warm clothes

사과 수확 - apple picking

스케이트를 타다 - to skate

스키를 타다 - to ski

소풍을 가다 - to picnic

어디에 가요? [Where do you go?]

공원 - a park

캠핑장 - a campsite

스케이트장 - a skating rink

해변 - the beach

하이킹 코스 - a hiking trail

산 - a mountain

강 - a river

호수 - a lake

바다 - the ocean; the beach

왜 좋아해요? [Why do you like it?]

덥다 - to be hot

따뜻하다 - to be warm

춥다 - to be cold

시원하다 - to be cool

바람이 불다 - windy; breezy

맑다 - to be sunny/clear

눈이 오다 - to snow

비가 오다 - to rain

흐리다 - to be cloudy

날씨 - the weather

쌀쌀하다 - to be chilly

예쁘다 - to be pretty

누구랑 같이 보내요? [Who do you spend it with?]

엄마/어머니 - mom/mother

오빠 - older brother [F]

언니 - older sister [F]

아빠/아버지 - dad/father

형 - older brother [M]

누나 - older sister [M]

부모님 - parents

할아버지 - grandfather

할머니 - grandmother

동생 - a younger sibling

사촌 - a cousin

친척 - a relative

친한 친구 - close friend(s)

애인 - a partner; lover

혼자(서) - alone; by oneself

남자친구 - a boyfriend

여자친구 - a girlfriend

지인 - an acquaintance

육하원칙

어떤 계절을 가장 좋아하세요?
[eo-tteon gye-jeo-reul ga-jang jo-a-ha-se-yo?]

Developing Your Answer

뭘 할 수 있어요?	What can you do?
봄에는 에쁜 꽃을 볼 수 있어요.	[You can see pretty flowers in spring]
여름에는 바다에서 수영해요.	[In summer I swim in the ocean.]
가을에는 단풍을 볼 수 있어요.	[In fall you can see the fall colors.]
겨울에는 눈사람을 만들 수 있어요.	[In winter you can make a snowman.]
여름에는 수박을 먹어요.	[I eat watermelon in summer.]

Your Turn:

어디에 가요?	Where do you go?
여름에는 해변에 가요.	[In summer I go to the beach.]
가을에는 캠핑장에 가요.	[In fall I go to a campsite.]
겨울에는 스케이트장에 가요.	[I go to a skating rink in winter.]
봄에는 한강에 벚꽃 구경을 가요.	[I view cherry blossoms in spring at the Han River.]
봄에는 공원에 소풍을 가요.	[In spring I picnic at the park.]

Your Turn:

육하원칙

어떤 계절을 가장 좋아하세요?
[eo-tteon gye-jeo-reul ga-jang jo-a-ha-se-yo?]

Developing Your Answer

왜 좋아해요?	Why do you like it?
봄은 너무 덥지 않아서 좋아해요.	[I like spring since it's not too hot.]
여름에는 아이스크림을 많이 먹어요.	[I eat lots of ice cream in the summer.]
가을에는 사과를 수확할 수 있어요.	[I can go apple picking in the fall.]
겨울에는 예쁜 코트를 입어요.	[I wear pretty coats in the winter.]
겨울에는 핫초코를 마셔요.	[I drink hot chocolate in the winter.]

Your Turn:

누구랑 같이 보내요?	Who do you spend it with?
가족이랑 같이 해변에 가요.	[I go to the beach with my family.]
겨울마다 친구랑 스케이트를 타요.	[I skate with friends every winter.]
언니랑 같이 캠핑을 가요.	[I go camping with my older sister.]
애인이랑 공원에 소풍을 가요.	[I picnic at the park with my partner.]
혼자서 벚꽃 구경하는 걸 좋아해요.	[I like viewing cherry blossoms by myself.]

Your Turn:

쓰기

어떤 계절을 가장 좋아하세요?
[eo-tteon gye-jeo-reul ga-jang jo-a-ha-se-yo?]

Try Writing Your Own Answer

1) Write your own answer below to the question   --   어떤 계절을 가장 좋아하세요? --

2) Get your answer corrected and rewrite your corrected answer here:

You can post your writing on an app/website like *Hellotalk* or *Hinative* for free corrections.

대화

어떤 계절을 가장 좋아하세요?
[eo-tteon gye-jeo-reul ga-jang jo-a-ha-se-yo?]

Example Conversation

지수: 이제 장마철이네요. 보라씨, 장마철을 좋아해요?
It's the rainy season now. Bora, do you like the rainy season?

보라: 네! 좋아해요. 지수씨는요?
Yeah! I like it. How about you, Jisu?

지수: 글쎄요. 장마철은 싫**지도 않**지만 좋**지도 않아요**. 왜 좋아해요?
I'm not sure. I don't dislike the rainy season, but I don't like it either. Why do you like it?

보라: 장마철에 파전이랑 막걸리를 먹는 걸 좋아해요.
I like to eat Pajeon and drink Makkeolli during the rainy season.

지수: 네, 저도요. 하지만 장마철에는 모기가 너무 많아요. 그리고 습도가 높고 저는 비를 맞는 것을 좋아하**지 않아요**.
Yeah, me too. But in the rainy season, there are so many mosquitoes. Plus it's humid, and I don't like getting rained on.

보라: 아, 그래서 저는 주로 집에 있어요. 하하
Ah, that's why I just stay at home. Haha.

문화

어떤 계절을 가장 좋아하세요?
[eo-tteon gye-jeo-reul ga-jang jo-a-ha-se-yo?]

Culture Note

장마철

Korea experiences all four seasons, but it is often said that they have a fifth season: 장마철. 장마철 means "monsoon season", or "the rainy season" and it's a long period of heavy rain lasting from around mid-June to mid-July. The severity of 장마철 varies from year to year, but on average more than half of the annual precipitation for the year falls during the 장마 season [10]. The air is hot and humid, with a mean temperature of about 73°- 79° Fahrenheit (23° - 26°C) [11].

A novel way to combat 장마철 is to use a machine that dispenses plastic umbrella covers, which can be found upon entry to most stores and public transport systems. One can swipe their wet umbrella through the machine (우산 비닐 포장기) to get a simple plastic cover (우산 비닐커버) for their umbrella, which prevents the umbrella from dripping all over the floor. As well as the heavy rainfall, some additional difficulties during 장마철 include mosquitoes, mold, and laundry that never dries.

It's common to have 파전 (savory pancakes) and 막걸리 (Korean rice wine) during 장마철. Many Koreans say that the sizzling sound the 파전 makes as it's getting fried reminds them of the sound of raindrops.

Q3

취미가 뭐예요?

[chwi-mi-ga mwo-e-yo?]

What are your hobbies?

취미 : hobby

~이/가 : subject particle

뭐 : what

~이에요/예요 : the copula "to be"

대답

취미가 뭐예요?
[chwi-mi-ga mwo-e-yo?]
What are your hobbies?

제 취미는 독서예요.

매일 판타지 소설을 읽어요.

그리고 한국어를 공부하는 것도 좋아하고 요리도 좋아해요.

My hobby is reading books.
I read fantasy novels every day.
I also like studying Korean, and I like cooking, too.

Answer Breakdown

Vocabulary	Grammar
Nouns	~은/는 Topic Particle
제: my	~을/를 Object Particle
취미: hobby	~이에요/예요
독서: reading (hobby)	Present Tense ~아/어요
매일: every day	V~는 것
판타지: fantasy	N~도
소설: novel(s)	그리고, 그래서 & 하지만
그리고: And (sentence starter)	A/V~고, N(이)고
한국어: Korean language	
요리: cooking	
Action Verbs	
읽다: to read	
공부하다: to study	
좋아하다: to like	

The grammar is color-coded to match chapters in *Conversational Korean Grammar*.

설명

Grammar Spotlight

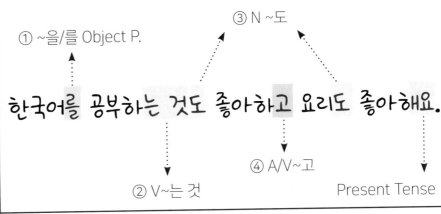

① ~을/를 Object P.

③ N ~도

② V~는 것

④ A/V~고

Present Tense

한국어를 공부하는 것도 좋아하고 요리도 좋아해요.

① **을/를 Object Particle**: ~을/를 attaches to a noun in order to show that the noun is the direct object in a sentence or clause. That is, the noun is an object that's acted on by the verb. Above, "한국어" (Korean) becomes "한국어를" as the object of the verb "공부하다" (to study).

매일 조금씩 그림을 그려요.　　　　　I draw a little bit every day.

영화를 자주 봐요.　　　　　　　　　I watch movies often.

② **V~는 것**: Attach ~는 것 to the verb stem of an action verb to use it as a noun in your sentence. The verb "공부하다" (to study) used above becomes the noun "공부하는 것" (studying). You can now talk about the characteristics/state of "studying" as you would any other noun.

운동을 하는 것은 건강에 좋아요.　　　Exercising is good for your health.

친구들하고 같이 게임하는 것을 좋아해요.　I like playing games with my friends.

③ **N~도**: The particle ~도 can attach to any noun in a sentence to say "also N" or "N too." It appears in the above sentence as 공부하는 것도 "also studying" and 요리도 "cooking too".

저는 사진 찍는 것도 좋아해요.　　　　I like taking photos, too.

저는 레코드판을 수집하는 것도 좋아해요.　I also like collecting vinyl records.

④ **A/V~고**: ~고 attaches to the verb stem, and is used to connect two clauses in a sentence together with the meaning "and". Just attach ~고 to the final verb in the first clause. The example above shows clause 1: "한국어를 공부하는것도 좋아하다" (to also like studying Korean) and clause 2: "요리도 좋아하다." (to also like cooking). They are connected using the final verb in the first clause "좋아하다", which becomes "좋아하고..." (I like it and...)

테니스도 치고 축구도 해요.　　　　　I play tennis and I also play soccer.

친구를 만나서 영화도 보고 밥도 먹어요.　I meet my friends and we watch movies and eat.

문법

V~는 것
[For turning verbs into nouns]

Grammar Practice

V~는 것
This form nominalizes an action verb; that is, it changes a verb into its noun form. Attaching **~는 것** to a verb stem lets you describe or act upon the verb as a noun.

Scan the QR code to view a short grammar lesson PDF.

Given the English sentence below, use the grammar form above to write the equivalent expression in Korean.

1. Reading often is important.　　　　읽다 - to read | 중요하다 - important

....

2. Walking is good for your health.　　걷다 - to walk | 건강 - health | 좋다 - good

....

3. I like studying Korean.　　　　　　공부하다 - to study | 좋아하다 - to like

....

4. Playing the piano is difficult.　　　피아노를 치다 - to play piano | *어렵다 - difficult

....

5. Exercising is difficult, but fun.　　운동하다 - to exercise | 재미있다 - fun

....

*Irregular Verb: Be aware that this verb conjugates irregularly.

ANSWERS: 1. 자주 읽는 것은 중요해요.   2. 걷는 것은 건강에 좋아요.   3. 저는 한국어를 공부하는 것을 좋아해요.   4. 피아노를 치는 것은 어려워요.   5. 운동하는 것은 어렵지만 재미있어요.

Please be aware that not all sentences have one exact translation, so answers may vary slightly.

어휘

취미가 뭐예요?
[chwi-mi-ga mwo-e-yo?]

Recommended Vocabulary

취미가 뭐예요? [What are your hobbies?]

독서 - reading (hobby)

영화감상 - watching movies

음악감상 - listening to music

명상 - meditation

스포츠 - sports

운동 - exercise

등산 - hiking

만화책 - comics/manga

게임을 하다 - to play games

식물을 기르다 - to grow plants

사진을 찍다 - to take pictures

요리하다 - to cook

자전거를 타다 - to ride a bike

그림을 그리다 - to draw

수집하다 - to collect

연습하다 - to practice

만들다 - to make

배우다 - to learn

이 취미를 언제 시작했어요? [When did you start this hobby?]

시작하다 - to start

10살 - 10 years old

최근 - recently

얼마 안 됐다 - it hasn't been long

2년 - 2 years

쯤 - about; around; approx.

취미를 얼마나 자주 해요? [How often do you do your hobby?]

항상 - always

자주 - often

가끔 - sometimes

거의 안 (하다) - rarely (do it)

아침 - morning; breakfast

저녁 - evening; dinner

밤 - night

매일 - every day

주말 - weekend

(1시간) 동안 - for (1 hour)

하루에 5분씩 - for 5 minutes a day

시간이 있을 때 - when I have time

이 취미를 왜 좋아해요? [Why do you like this hobby?]

그냥 - just; only; simply

재미있다 - fun; interesting

비싸지 않다 - not expensive

건강에 좋다 - to be good for one's health

스트레스가 풀리다 - to relieve stress

성취감을 느끼다 - to feel a sense of accomplishment

육하원칙

취미가 뭐예요?
[chwi-mi-ga mwo-e-yo?]

Developing Your Answer

취미가 뭐예요?	What are your hobbies?
제 취미는 영화 감상이에요.	[My hobby is watching movies.]
저는 레코드판을 수집해요.	[I collect vinyl records.]
제 취미는 피아노 연습이에요.	[My hobby is practicing the piano.]
제 취미는 등산이랑 스포츠예요.	[My hobbies are hiking and sports.]
제 취미는 자전거를 타는 거예요.	[My hobby is riding my bicycle.]

Your Turn:

....

....

....

이 취미를 언제 시작했어요?	When did you start this hobby?
시작한지 2년쯤 됐어요.	[It's been 2 years since I started.]
한국어를 배운지 얼마 안 됐어요.	[I haven't been learning Korean long.]
10살 때부터 요리하는 걸 좋아했어요.	[I've liked cooking since I was 10.]
그림을 그리는 걸 항상 좋아했어요.	[I've always liked drawing.]
최근에 식물을 기르기 시작했어요.	[I recently started growing plants.]

Your Turn:

....

....

....

육하원칙

취미가 뭐예요?
[chwi-mi-ga mwo-e-yo?]

Developing Your Answer

취미를 얼마나 자주 해요?	How often do you do your hobby?
자주 베이킹하고 요리를 해요.	[I bake and cook often.]
매일 아침마다 명상을 해요.	[I meditate every morning.]
주말마다 사진을 찍어요.	[I take pictures every weekend.]
매일 30분씩 기타를 쳐요.	[I play guitar for 30 minutes every day.]
시간이 있을 때마다 게임을 해요.	[I play games whenever I have time.]

Your Turn:

이 취미를 왜 좋아해요?	Why do you like this hobby?
운동하는 것은 건강에 좋아요.	[Exercising is good for your health.]
한국어를 공부하는 게 재미있어요.	[Studying Korean is fun.]
저는 성취감을 느낄 수 있어요.	[I can feel a sense of accomplishment.]
스트레스가 풀려서 좋아요.	[It's good for relieving my stress.]
그냥 재미있는 것 같아요.	[I just think it's fun.]

Your Turn:

쓰기

취미가 뭐예요?
[chwi-mi-ga mwo-e-yo?]

Try Writing Your Own Answer

1) Write your own answer below to the question -- 취미가 뭐예요? --

2) Get your answer corrected and rewrite your corrected answer here:

대화

취미가 뭐예요?
[chwi-mi-ga mwo-e-yo?]

Example Conversation

소피: 하람씨, 취미가 뭐예요?
What are your hobbies, Haram?

하람: 저는 만화를 좋아해요! 그래서 만화를 많이 봐요.
I like comics! So I read a lot of comic books.

소피: 만화방에 가 본 적이 있어요?
Have you been to a manhwabang (lit. a "comic room")?

하람: 네 물론이죠. 집 근처에 괜찮은 만화방이 있어서 가끔 친구랑 같이 가요. 소피씨는 취미가 뭐예요?
Yes of course. There's a good manhwabang near my house, so sometimes I go with my friends. What are your hobbies, Sophie?

소피: 저는 노래를 좋아해요. 그래서 노래방에 종종 가요.
I like singing. So now and then I go to a noraebang (lit. "singing room"/karaoke).

하람: 아, 그래요. 저도 노래방에 **가는 것**을 좋아해요. 하지만 간지 오래 됐어요.
Ah, I see. I like going to noraebangs too. But it's been a while since I've gone.

소피: 이번 주말에 저랑 노래방에 갈래요?
Would you like to go to a noraebang with me this weekend?

하람: 네, 좋아요!
Sounds good!

문화

취미가 뭐예요?
[chwi-mi-ga mwo-e-yo?]

Culture Note

방

A 방 - literally translating to "room" - is a place where people can go and enjoy some form of entertainment. There are many different types of "방" in Korea.

노래방 (noraebang): These rooms are for Korean karaoke. It is common for groups of friends or co-workers to go to a noraebang after school or work as a fun way to relax. You can have food delivered to your room and sing pop songs to your heart's content.

찜질방 (jjimjilbang): A jjimjilbang is a Korean bathhouse. There are saunas, hot and/or cold pools, and rooms for skin scrubs and massage. These saunas are separated by gender, and clothing in these areas is optional (with most preferring to go without). Many bathhouses also have a lounge area and a cafeteria. They provide loungewear and allow people to sleep overnight for a nominal fee, although accommodations are minimal.

만화방 (manhwabang): A manhwabang is a place that sells comic books (manga/anime), with cozy places to relax and read your favorite comics. Some even have places to buy fresh coffee and snacks, bean bags to sit in, and even comfy reading nooks to curl up in.

Q4

베이킹을 할 수 있어요?

[be-i-king-eul hal su i-sseo-yo?]

Can you bake?

베이킹: baking;   베이킹을 하다 : to bake, to do baking

~을/를 : object particle

V + ~ㄹ/을 수 있다: used to talk about ability; "can"

~아요/어요: informal polite present tense

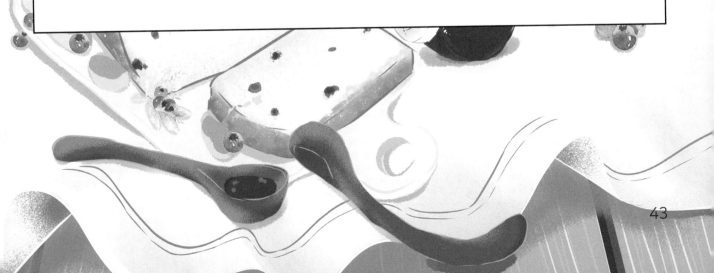

대답

베이킹을 할 수 있어요?
[be-i-king-eul hal su i-sseo-yo?]
Can you bake?

아니요, 베이킹을 잘 못 해요.
자주 연습해도 이제까지 안든 것들을 다 망쳤어요.
베이킹을 잘 하고 싶지만 아직도 어려워요.

No, I can't bake very well.
Even though I practice often, I've ruined everything I've made before now.
I want to be good at baking, but I still find it difficult.

Answer Breakdown

Vocabulary	Grammar
Nouns	~을/를 Object Particle
아니요 - no	Present Tense ~아/어요
베이킹 - baking	N~부터 & N~까지
자주 - often	N~들
이제 - now; nowadays	A/V~았/었어요 Past Tense
것 - thing; object	N~도
다 - everything; all	잘 & 잘 못 V
아직 - still; yet; now	Words of Frequency
Action Verbs	V~고 싶다
베이킹을 하다 - to bake (i.e. 'to do baking')	A/V~지만, N(이)지만
연습하다 - to practice	V~은 N
만들다 - to make	A/V~아/어도, N(이)라도
망치다 - to ruin; to fail (at)	
Descriptive Verbs	
어렵다 - to be difficult/hard	

The grammar is color-coded to match chapters in *Conversational Korean Grammar*.

설명

Grammar Spotlight

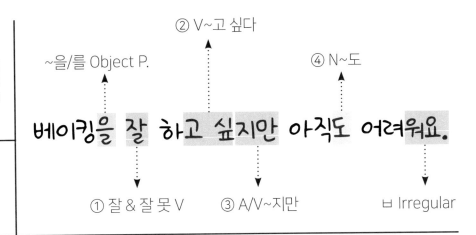

② V~고 싶다

~을/를 Object P.

④ N~도

베이킹을 잘 하고 싶지만 아직도 어려워요.

① 잘 & 잘 못 V

③ A/V~지만

ㅂ Irregular

① **잘 & 잘 못 V**: 잘 means "well" or "good". It is an adverb that's used to describe HOW an action is done. It appears before action verbs, e.g. "**잘** 가르쳐요" (I teach well). **못** means "can't". It can be combined with **잘** to say "not well," e.g. "**잘 못** 가르쳐요" (I can't teach well). For seperable verbs like "수영하다" (to swim) which combines the noun "수영" (swimming) and the verb "하다" (to do), place **잘 & 잘 못** between the two parts, e.g."수영을 **잘** 해요" (I swim well).

쿠키를 **잘** 만들어요.　　　　　　　　　I'm good at making cookies.
케이크를 **잘 못** 만들어요.　　　　　　　I can't make cakes well.

② **~고 싶다**: Attach **~고 싶다** to the stem of any action verb to say you want to do that verb. The sentence above uses the verb "베이킹을 하다" (to bake), and when you attach this form to the verb stem, it becomes "배이킹을 하**고 싶어요**." (I want to bake).

빵을 잘 만들**고 싶어요**.　　　　　　　I want to be good at making bread.
레시피대로 잘 만들**고 싶어요**.　　　　I want to make it just like the recipe.

③ **A/V~지만**: Attach **~지만** to the verb stem of a descriptive or action verb when you want to contrast two clauses in a sentence with the meaning of "but." Just add it to the final verb in the first clause, e.g. "베이킹을 잘 하고 싶**지만**..." (I want to bake well, but...)

레시피대로 만들고 싶**지만** 잘 안 돼요.　　　I want to follow the recipe, but it turns out wrong.
베이킹을 시작하고 싶**지만** 시간이 없어요.　　I want to start baking, but I don't have time.

④ **N~도**: **~도** can be attached to some nouns to add emphasis. The word "아직" means "still," and adding **~도** to it here makes the feeling of "still" even stronger, i.e. "even still."

베이킹 학원에 가지만 **아직도** 잘 못해요.　　　I'm going to baking classes, but I'm still bad at it.
베이킹을 자주 하지만 **아직도** 많이 실수해요.　I bake often, but I still make lots of mistakes.

문법

V ~(으)ㄹ 수 있다/없다
[For talking about things you can/can't do]

Grammar Practice

V~(으)ㄹ 수 있다/없다
Attach this form to an action verb stem to talk about ability. Attach ~(으)ㄹ 수 있다 to say "(subject) can" and attach ~(으)ㄹ 수 없다 to say "(subject) can't."

Scan the QR code to view a short grammar lesson PDF.

Given the English sentence below, use the grammar form above to write the equivalent expression in Korean.

1. I can play the piano.

피아노 - piano | 치다 - to play (piano)

2. I'm really tired, but I can't sleep.

너무 - really | 피곤하다 - tired | 자다 - to sleep

3. I can read Korean.

한국어 - Korean | 읽다 - to read

4. I can also eat spicy foods well.

매운 음식 - spicy foods | 잘 - well | 먹다 - eat

5. I can make cookies well.

쿠키 - cookies | 만들다 - to make

ANSWERS: 1. 저는 피아노를 칠 수 있어요. 2. 저는 너무 피곤하지만 잘 수 없어요. 3. 저는 한국어를 읽을 수 있어요. 4. 저는 매운 음식도 잘 먹을 수 있어요. 5. 저는 쿠키를 잘 만들 수 있어요.

Please be aware that not all sentences have one exact translation, so answers may vary slightly.

어휘

베이킹을 할 수 있어요?
[be-i-king-eul hal su i-sseo-yo?]

Recommended Vocabulary

베이킹해 본 적이 있어요? [Have you ever baked?]

케이크- a cake

컵케이크- a cupcake

머핀 - a muffin

파이 - a pie

빵 - bread

페이스트리 - a pastry

쿠키 - a cookie

처음 - the first time

한번 - once

만들다 - to make

굽다 - to bake (something)

베이킹을 하다 - to do baking

종종 - now and then

배우다 - to learn

직접 - firsthand; in person

베이킹을 잘 해요? [Are you good at baking?]

금손 - gifted/talented at

똥손 - terrible at

서투르다 - clumsy; unskilled

못 하다 - unable to do

잘 하다 - to do well

능력이 있다 - to be capable

능력이 없다 - to be incapable

실력이 좋다 - to be skilled at

실력이 나쁘다 - unskilled at

레시피 - a recipe

따라하다 - to follow

사용하다 - to use

언제 베이킹을 해요? [When do you bake?]

휴일 - a rest day; a day off

주말 - weekend

생일 - birthday

시간이 있다 - to have time

한가하다 - free (not busy)

가끔 - sometimes

자주 - often

항상 - always

별로 (+ negative) - not really

거의 (+ negative) - rarely

절대 (+ negative) - never

명절 - a national holiday

왜 베이킹을 하는 것을 좋아해요? [Why do you like to bake?]

시간이 걸리다 - to take time

맛있다 - to be delicious

재미있다 - fun; interesting

같이/함께 - together

어렵다 - to be difficult/hard

주다 - to give

스트레스가 풀리다 - to relieve stress

마음이 편하다 - to be relax-ing

뿌듯하다 - to be proud/ac-complished

육하원칙

베이킹을 할 수 있어요?
[be-i-king-eul hal su i-sseo-yo?]

Developing Your Answer

베이킹해 본 적이 있어요?	Have you ever baked?
케이크를 만들어 본 적이 있어요.	[I've made a cake before.]
한번도 베이킹해 본 적이 없어요.	[I've never once baked.]
어제 처음으로 쿠키를 구워 봤어요.	[Yesterday I baked cookies for the first time.]
저는 집에서 종종 빵을 만들어요.	[I make homemade bread from time to time.]
페이스트리를 잘 구울 수 있어요.	[I'm good at baking pastries.]

Your Turn:

베이킹을 잘 해요?	Are you good at baking?
베이킹을 잘 하는 편이에요.	[I'm pretty good at baking.]
저는 베이킹 똥손이에요.	[I'm terrible at baking.]
저는 베이킹을 잘 못 하지만 좋아해요.	[I'm not very good at it, but I like baking.]
저는 그냥 그래요.	[I'm just so-so.]
베이킹은 할 일이 많아서 싫어요.	[I don't like baking, because it's a lot of work.]

Your Turn:

육하원칙

베이킹을 할 수 있어요?
[be-i-king-eul hal su i-sseo-yo?]

Developing Your Answer

언제 베이킹을 해요?	When do you bake?
스트레스를 받을 때 베이킹을 해요.	[I bake when I'm stressed.]
명절에 주로 베이킹을 해요.	[I mainly bake on holidays.]
주말에 빵을 만들어요.	[I make bread on the weekend.]
친구 생일에 케이크를 만들어요.	[I make cakes for my friend's birthdays.]
가끔 머핀을 굽지만 자주는 안 해요.	[I make muffins sometimes, but not often.]

Your Turn:

....

....

....

왜 베이킹을 하는 것을 좋아해요?	Why do you like to bake?
애인하고 같이 베이킹할 수 있어서요.	[Because I can bake with my partner.]
엄마의 레시피가 정말 맛있어서요.	[Because my mom's recipes are really delicious.]
친구한테 빵을 주는 걸 좋아해요.	[I like giving bread to my friends.]
베이킹을 하면 스트레스가 풀려요.	[When I bake, it relieves my stress.]
어렵고 시간이 많이 걸려서 안 해요.	[It's hard and it takes a lot of time, so I don't do it.]

Your Turn:

....

....

....

쓰기

베이킹을 할 수 있어요?
[be-i-king-eul hal su i-sseo-yo?]

Try Writing Your Own Answer

1) Write your own answer below to the question -- 베이킹을 할 수 있어요? --

2) Get your answer corrected and rewrite your corrected answer here:

대화

베이킹을 할 수 있어요?
[be-i-king-eul hal su i-sseo-yo?]

Example Conversation

사라: 희진 씨, 베이킹을 할 수 있어요?
Can you bake, Heejin?

희진: 사실 토요일에 첫 베이킹 수업을 가요. 같이 갈래요?
Actually, I'm going to my first baking class on Saturday. Would you like to go too?

사라: 오, 재미있겠다. 근데 저는 베이킹을 못 해요. 그래도 괜찮아요?
Oh, that sounds fun. But I can't bake. Would it still be okay?

희진: 네, 괜찮아요! 저도 못 해요! 토스트만 만들 수 있어요. 베이킹을 잘 하고 싶어요.
Yes, that's okay! I can't bake either! I can only make toast. I want to get good at baking.

사라: 그럼 좋아요! 같이 가고 싶어요. 수업에서 뭘 배워요? 커스터드번? 계란빵? 그리고 수업은 어디에요?
Sounds good then! I'd like to go with you. What will we learn in class? Custard buns? Egg bread? Also where is the class?

희진: 커스터드번인 것 같아요. 그리고 수업은 동네 빵집에 있어요. 같이 갈 수 있으면 좋겠어요.
I think it'll be custard buns. And the class is at the local bakery. I hope we can go together.

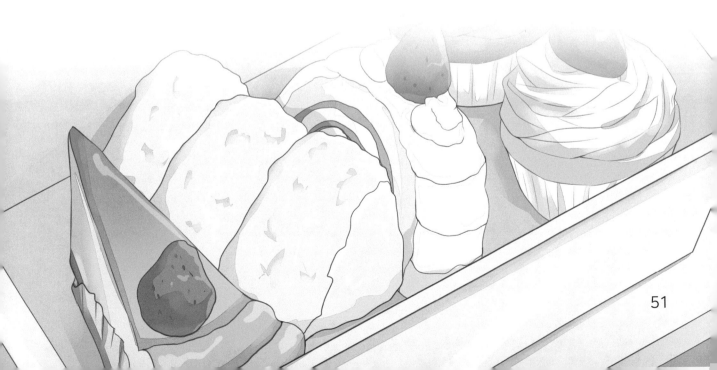

51

문화

베이킹을 할 수 있어요?
[be-i-king-eul hal su i-sseo-yo?]

Culture Note

빵집

Bread was first brought to Korea by foreign missionaries in the late 19th century. Due to later events, including the Korean War, the aid of raw ingredients by the US government, and a policy that encouraged flour consumption in the 1960s, the Korean bakery industry began to flourish. In fact, in 2018, Korean people ate 21g of bread per day on average. [12]

One of the largest bakery chain stores in Korea is *Paris Baguette*, which has 3,600 stores in Korea and has also expanded into other countries like China and the US. [13]

Korean bakeries (빵집) like *Paris Baguette* offer a unique fusion of Korean, Japanese, and French baking styles, mixing traditional pastries with Korean flavors like red bean, sesame seed, green tea, and sweet potato.

There are hundreds of Korean bakery items, but some staples include 계란빵 (egg bread), 찹쌀도넛 (glutinous rice donut), 커스터드번 (custard bun), 붕어빵 (fish-shaped bread), 소보로빵 (peanut streussel buns), and 소시지빵 (hot dog pastries).

Q5

무엇으로 하루를 시작해요?

[mu-eo-seu-ro ha-ru-reul shi-jak-hae-yo?]

What do you do to start your day?

무엇 : what

~(으)로 : "by, with, using" particle

하루 : a day

~을/를 : object particle

시작하다 : to start; to begin

~아요/어요: informal polite present tense

대답

무엇으로 하루를 시작해요?
[mu-eo-seu-ro ha-ru-reul shi-jak-hae-yo?]
What do you do to start your day?

매일 아침 스트레칭으로 하루를 시작해요.
그 다음에 항상 커피 한 잔을 마셔요.
커피 없는 아침을 상상할 수 없어요.

I start my day by stretching every morning.
After that I always drink a cup of coffee.
I can't imagine my morning without coffee.

Answer Breakdown

Vocabulary	Grammar
Nouns	~을/를 Object Particle
매일 - every day	Present Tense ~아/어요
아침 - morning; breakfast	N~(으)로
스트레칭 - stretching	Words of Frequency
하루 - a day	A~ㄴ/은/는 N
그 - that	V~(으)ㄹ 수 있다/없다
항상 - always	N 다음에
커피 - coffee	
한 잔 - one cup	
Action Verbs	
시작하다 - to start	
마시다 - to drink	
상상하다 - to imagine	
Descriptive Verbs	
없다 - to not exist; to not have	

The grammar is color-coded to match chapters in *Conversational Korean Grammar*.

설명

Grammar Spotlight

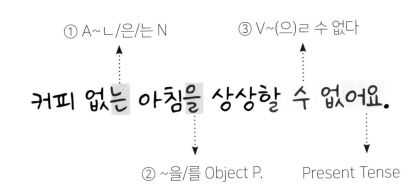

① A~ㄴ/은/는 N

③ V~(으)ㄹ 수 없다

커피 없는 아침을 상상할 수 없어요.

② ~을/를 Object P.

Present Tense

---

① A~ㄴ/은/는 N: the verb "없다" is a descriptive verb meaning "to not have; be absent." There-fore "커피(가) 없다" is "to not have coffee." The subject particle is optional but not required. To turn descriptive verbs into their adjective forms (so that you can describe the morning as not having coffee) you add "ㄴ/은/는" to the verb stem. When using 있다 or 없다 verbs, you always attach "~는". Now it becomes "커피 없**는** 아침" (a morning without coffee).

건강**한** 아침식사를 먹는 것을 좋아해요.　　　I like to eat a healthy breakfast.

따뜻**한** 샤워로 하루를 시작해요.　　　　　　I start my day with a hot shower.

② 을/를 Object Particle: ~을/를 attaches to a noun in order to show that the noun is the direct object in a sentence or clause. That is, the noun is an object that's acted on by the verb. In the above sentence, the noun phrase "커피 없는 아침" (a morning without coffee) is connect-ed to the verb "상상하다" (to imagine) using the ~을/를 object particle.

아침에 가벼운 운동**을** 자주 해요.　　　　　　　I often do light exercise in the morning.

쌀쌀한 아침에 일찍 일어나는 것**을** 싫어해요.　I don't like getting up early on chilly mornings.

③ V~(으)ㄹ 수 있다/없다: this grammar form attaches to action verb stems to talk about verbs that you can/cannot do. You can use V~(으)ㄹ 수 있다 to talk about things you can do, and V~(으)ㄹ 수 없다 to talk about things you cannot do. In the example above, the verb "상상하다" (to imagine) becomes "상상**할 수 없어요**" (I cannot imagine).

늦잠 자는 아침을 상상**할 수 없어요**.　　　　I can't imagine a morning where I sleep in.

아침밥 없는 하루를 상상**할 수 없어요**.　　　I can't imagine a day without breakfast.

문법

A/V~(으)면
[For connecting clauses with "if/when"]

Grammar Practice

A/V~(으)면
This form connects two clauses in a sentence with the meaning of "if" or "when." Attach **~으면** if the verb stem ends with a consonant, and **~면** if it ends with a vowel.

Scan the QR code to view a short grammar lesson PDF.

Given the English sentence below, use the grammar form above to write the equivalent expression in Korean.

1. When it's hot, I eat icecream.

*덥다 - hot | 아이스크림 - icecream | 먹다 - eat

....

2. When it's cold, I wear a coat.

*춥다 - cold | 코트 - coat | 입다 - wear

....

3. If I have time, I'll exercise.

시간 - time | 있다 - have | 운동하다 - exercise

....

4. If it rains tomorrow, I won't go.

내일 - tomorrow | 비가 오다 - rain | 가다 - go

....

5. When I eat delicious food, I'm happy.

맛있는 음식 - delicious food | 기분이 좋다 - happy

....

*Irregular Verb: Be aware that this verb conjugates irregularly.

ANSWERS: 1. 더우면 아이스크림을 먹어요. 2. 추우면 코트를 입어요. 3. 시간이 있으면 운동해요. 4. 내일 비가 오면 안 갈 거예요./가지 않을 거예요. 5. 맛있는 음식을 먹으면 기분이 좋아요.

Please be aware that not all sentences have one exact translation, so answers may vary slightly.

어휘

무엇으로 하루를 시작해요?
[mu-eo-seu-ro ha-ru-reul shi-jak-hae-yo?]

Recommended Vocabulary

무엇으로 하루를 시작해요? [What do you do to start your day?]

하루 - a/the day

시작하다 - to start

먼저 - first

끄다 - to turn sth off

켜다 - to turn sth on

일기를 쓰다 - to journal

마시다 - to drink

스트레칭하다 - to stretch

샤워하다 - to shower

일어나다 - wake up; get up

깨우다 - to wake sbdy up

확인하다 - to check

양치질을 하다 - to brush one's teeth

세수하다 - to wash one's face

침대를 정리하다 - to make one's bed

아침 일과를 바꾸고 싶어요? [Do you want to change your morning routine?]

아침 일과 - morning routine

늦잠을 자다 - to sleep in; to oversleep

일찍 - early

운동을 하다 - to exercise

식사하다 - to have a meal

요가를 하다 - to do yoga

명상을 하다 - to meditate

대신 - instead of; rather

목표를 세우다 - to set goals

언제 하루를 시작해요? [When do you start your day?]

아침 - morning; breakfast

밤 - night

오전 - a.m.; the morning

오후 - p.m.; the afternoon

준비하다 - to get ready

늦다 - to be late

녹차 - green tea

커피 - coffee

쯤 - about; around; approx.

아침 일과에서 뭐가 제일 좋아요? [What's the best part of your morning routine?]

출근하다 - to go to work

신문 - a newspaper

해가 뜨다 - the sun rises

힘이 나다 - to gain energy

최고 - the best

맛있다 - to be delicious

강아지 - a dog/puppy

산책하다 - to go for a walk

침대 - bed

뒹굴거리다 - to laze; to lay around; be a couch potato

하루 종일 - all day

좋다 - to be good; likeable

육하원칙

무엇으로 하루를 시작해요?
[mu-eo-seu-ro ha-ru-reul shi-jak-hae-yo?]

Developing Your Answer

무엇으로 하루를 시작해요?	What do you do to start your day?
샤워하는 걸로 하루를 시작해요.	[I start my day by taking a shower.]
저는 먼저 핸드폰을 확인해요.	[First, I check my phone.]
일어나자마자 물을 마셔요.	[I drink water right after I get up.]
먼저 양치질을 하고 세수해요.	[First I brush my teeth and wash my face.]
먼저 하는 일은 침대를 정리해요.	[The very first thing I do is make my bed.]

Your Turn:

아침 일과를 바꾸고 싶어요?	Do you want to change your morning routine?
네, 조금 더 일찍 일어나고 싶어요.	[Yes, I want to get up a little earlier.]
매일 아침 운동을 해야 해요.	[I should exercise every morning.]
항상 식사를 하면 좋을 것 같아요.	[I think it'd be good to always eat breakfast.]
핸드폰 대신 책을 봐야 돼요.	[I should read a book instead of looking at my phone.]
요가로 하루를 시작하고 싶어요.	[I want to start my day with yoga.]

Your Turn:

육하원칙

무엇으로 하루를 시작해요?
[mu-eo-seu-ro ha-ru-reul shi-jak-hae-yo?]

Developing Your Answer

언제 하루를 시작해요?	When do you start your day?
아침 8시 반 쯤에 일어나요.	[I get up at around 8:30 in the morning.]
오전 7시에 일어나서 하루를 준비해요.	[I get up at 7am and get ready for the day.]
8시에 일어나서 녹차로 하루를 시작해요.	[I get up at 8, and start my day with a cup of tea.]
커피를 마신 후에 하루가 시작돼요.	[My day starts after I've had some coffee.]
밤에 일하니까 오후 늦게 하루가 시작돼요.	[I work nights, so my day starts late in the afternoon.]

Your Turn:

아침 일과에서 뭐가 제일 좋아요?	What's the best part of your morning routine?
출근하기 전에 침대에서 뒹굴거려요.	[I lay around in bed before going to work.]
저는 해가 뜨는 걸 볼 때 힘이 나요.	[I get energized when I watch the sun rise.]
맛있는 아침을 먹는 게 최고예요.	[Eating a delicious breakfast is the best.]
커피를 마시면서 신문을 읽는 게 좋아요.	[Reading the paper while I drink coffee is great.]
강아지하고 산책하는 게 제일 좋아요.	[I like taking a walk with my dog the most.]

Your Turn:

쓰기

무엇으로 하루를 시작해요?
[mu-eo-seu-ro ha-ru-reul shi-jak-hae-yo?]

Try Writing Your Own Answer

1) Write your own answer below to the question   -- 무엇으로 하루를 시작해요? --

2) Get your answer corrected and rewrite your corrected answer here:

You can post your writing on an app/website like *Hellotalk* or *Hinative* for free corrections.

대화

무엇으로 하루를 시작해요?
[mu-eo-seu-ro ha-ru-reul shi-jak-hae-yo?]

Example Conversation

지수: 하람씨, 무엇으로 하루를 시작해요?
Haram, what do you do to start your day?

하람: 저는 아침밥을 꼭 먹어야 돼요.
I definitely have to have breakfast.

지수: 아 그렇군요. 그럼 오늘 아침은 뭐 먹었어요?
Oh, that makes sense. Then what did you eat this morning?

하람: 오늘은 시간이 별로 없어서 그냥 빵하고 커피를 사 먹었어요.
I didn'thave much time today so I just got some bread and coffee.

지수: 그래요? 맛있겠다. 보통 여유가 더 있**으면** 뭘 먹어요?
Really? That sounds good. What do you usually eat when you have more time?

하람: 보통은 밥하고 국, 그리고 김치에다가 반찬 몇 개를 더 먹어요. 하람 씨는요?
I usually have rice and soup, and some sides along with kimchi. How about you?

지수: 와, 푸짐하게 먹는 편이네요. 저는 보통 아침을 안 먹지만 오늘은 조금 배고파서 토스트랑 커피를 먹었어요.
Wow, you usually have quite a lot. I don't usually eat breakfast, but today I was a little hungry, so I had toast and a coffee.

하람: 커피 좋죠. 저도 커피를 좋아해서 아침에 커피가 없**으면** 안 돼요.
Isn't coffee great? I love coffee too - I can't start my day without my morning coffee.

문화

무엇으로 하루를 시작해요?
[mu-eo-seu-ro ha-ru-reul shi-jak-hae-yo?]

Culture Note

아침밥

A traditional Korean 아침밥, or "morning meal," is basically a lighter version of the same foods you'd eat for lunch or dinner. This may include rice (밥), porridge (죽), a soup or stew, kimchi (김치), eggs (계란), pork belly (보쌈), and savory pancakes (전). [14]

The exact foods differ across regions and families, but Korea typically does not have specific foods that are only eaten for breakfast. These days, some people are foregoing a traditional Korean sit-down breakfast in favor of something quicker that can be easily taken to work, like fruit, bread, or a whole-grain powdered drink called 미수가루 (misu-ga-ru).

Coffee, smoothies, pastries, 토스트 (egg toast sandwiches), 삼각김밥 (triangle kimbap), and steamed or baked sweet potatoes are also popular to pick up on the go from convenience stores, bakeries, and street vendors.

여행하는 것을 좋아하세요?

[yeo-haeng-ha-neun geo-seul jo-a-ha-se-yo?]

Do you like traveling?

여행 : a trip/vacation   ;   **여행을 하다** : to travel

V **~는 것** : verb nominalization; used to change a verb into it's noun form

~을/를 : object particle

좋아하다 : to like

~(으)세요 : honorific present tense sentence ending

대답

여행하는 것을 좋아하세요?
[yeo-haeng-ha-neun geo-seul jo-a-ha-se-yo?]
Do you like traveling?

네! 저는 여행하는 것을 좋아해요.
여행할 때마다 새로운 곳의 신기한 문화를 경험할 수 있어요.
그리고 현지 음식을 먹어 보는 것도 좋아요!

Yes! I like traveling.
Every time I travel, I can experience the interesting culture of a new place.
And it's also nice to try the local foods!

Answer Breakdown

Vocabulary	Grammar
Nouns	~은/는 Topic Particle
네 - yes	~을/를 Object Particle
저 - I; me	V~는 것
곳 - place	A/V~아/어요 Present Tense
문화 - culture	N~도
그리고: And (sentence starter)	A~ㄴ/은/는 N
현지 음식 - local food(s)	그리고, 그래서 & 하지만
Action Verbs	A/V~ㄹ/을 때, N 때
여행하다 - to travel	N~의
좋아하다 - to like	V~(으)ㄹ 수 있다/없다
경험하다 - to experience	V~아/어 보다
먹다 - to eat	N~마다
Descriptive Verbs	
새롭다 - to be new	
신기하다 - to be amazing/cool/novel	
좋다 - to be good; likeable	

The grammar is color-coded to match chapters in *Conversational Korean Grammar*.

설명

Grammar Spotlight

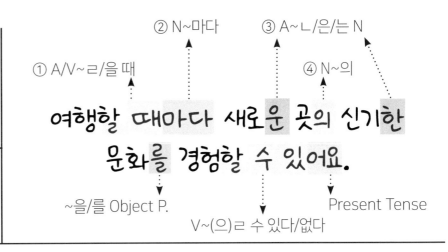

① A/V~ㄹ/을 때

② N~마다

③ A~ㄴ/은/는 N

④ N~의

여행할 때마다 새로운 곳의 신기한
문화를 경험할 수 있어요.

~을/를 Object P.

V~(으)ㄹ 수 있다/없다

Present Tense

① **A/V~ㄹ/을 때:** The word "**때**" refers to a specific "time" during some event or period. The form **~ㄹ/을 때** can be placed after a verb to mean "the time that" or "when" that verb happens. In the example above "여행하다" (to travel) becomes "여행**할 때**..." (when I travel...).

여행**할 때** 행복해요.	I'm happy when I travel.
비행기 **탈 때** 신나요.	I'm excited when I take a plane.

② **N~마다:** This form means "each/every/all," and it can be attached to a noun to say "every N." When attached to time nouns, it indicates that some action or situation repeats over a period of time. In the sentence above, **~마다** attaches to the noun "때"(when/a time), which is a part of the form ~ㄹ/을 때, ultimately creating "여행할 때**마다**" (every time I travel).

비행기를 탈 때**마다** 무서워요.	I'm scared every time I take a plane.
출장 갈 때**마다** 기념품을 사요.	Every time I go on a business trip I buy souvenirs.

③ **A~ㄴ/은/는 N:** Attach **~ㄴ/은/는** to a descriptive verb stem to change it into an adjective. Then, place that adjective in front of a noun to describe it. Use **~ㄴ** when the stem ends in a vowel, use **~은** when the stem ends in a consonant, and use **~는** when the stem ends in "있다/없다." In the example above, "새롭다" (to be new) becomes "새로운 곳" (a new place).

여행을 갈 때마다 새로**운** 친구를 사귀어요.	I make new friends every time I travel.
외국에 갈 때마다 맛있**는** 현지 음식을 먹어요.	I try the tasty local dishes whenever I go abroad.

④ **N~의:** This particle is used to show possession. It is similar to the way we use "X's" or "The Y of X" in English. In the sentence above "문화" (culture) belongs to "곳" (a place), so it is written as "곳**의** 문화" (the culture of a place/a place's culture)

휴양지**의** 따뜻한 날씨를 즐겨요.	I enjoy the resort's warm weather.
유명한 관광지**의** 기념품을 사요.	I buy souvenirs of famous tourist attractions.

문법

A~ㄴ/은/는 N
[For turning descriptive verbs into adjectives]

Grammar Practice

A~ㄴ/은/는 N

This form allows a descriptive verb to be placed as an adjective in front of the noun it describes. Attach ~ㄴ after a vowel, ~은 after a consonant, and ~는 after 있다/없다.

Scan the QR code to view a short grammar lesson PDF.

Given the English sentence below, use the grammar form above to write the equivalent expression in Korean. **From this chapter forward we'll be dropping "저는."**

1. I bought some delicious food.

맛있다 - delicious | 음식 - food | 사다 - buy

2. I'm taking a difficult test tomorrow.

어렵다 - difficult | 시험을 보다 - take a test

3. I met a good friend in Korea.

좋다 - good | 친구 - friend | 만나다 - meet

4. Today is an important day.

오늘 - today | 중요하다 - important | 날 - day

5. I watched a sad movie yesterday.

슬프다 - sad | 영화 - movie | 보다 - to watch

ANSWERS: 1. 맛있는 음식을 샀어요. 2. 내일 어려운 시험을 봐요. 3. 한국에서 좋은 친구를 만났어요. 4. 오늘은 중요한 날이에요. 5. 어제 슬픈 영화를 봤어요.

Please be aware that not all sentences have one exact translation, so answers may vary slightly.

어휘

여행하는 것을 좋아하세요?
[yeo-haeng-ha-neun geo-seul jo-a-ha-se-yo?]

Recommended Vocabulary

여행하는 것을 좋아해요? [Do you like traveling?]

여행을 하다 - to travel

좋아하다 - to like

수학여행 - a school/field trip

단체 여행 - a group trip

배낭여행 - a backpacking trip

여행을 가다 - to go on a trip

싫다 - to be bad; unlikeable

관광여행 - a sightseeing trip

가족 여행 - a family trip

1박 2일의 여행 - a trip for 2 days and 1 night

힘들다 - difficult; hard; tiring

당일치기 여행 - a day trip

자동차 여행 - a road trip

출장 - a business trip

관심이 있다/없다 - to be interested/not interested in

어디로 여행을 가요? [Where do you usually travel to?]

주로 - mainly; mostly

다른 나라 - other country

새로운 곳 - a new place

바다 - the ocean; the beach

도시 - a city

국내 여행 - a domestic trip

머물다 - to stay (temporarily)

호텔 - a hotel

해외 여행 - an overseas trip

언제 여행을 가요? [When do you travel?]

가을 - autumn; fall

여름 - summer

휴가 - a break; a vacation (time off from work)

겨울 - winter

휴일 - a rest day; a day off

갔다오다 - to go and come back

봄 - spring

방학 - a school vacation

주말 - weekend

여행할 때 뭐 해요? [What do you do when you travel?]

휴양지 - a tropical resort

방문하다 - to visit

일광욕을 하다 - to sunbathe

유명하다 - to be famous

쉬다 - to rest/relax

미술관 - an art gallery

기념품 - a souvenir

구경하다 - to view/spectate

관광지 - sights; attractions

박물관- a museum

수영하다 - to swim

현지 음식 - local food(s)

육하원칙

여행하는 것을 좋아하세요?
[yeo-haeng-ha-neun geo-seul jo-a-ha-se-yo?]

Developing Your Answer

여행하는 것을 좋아해요?	Do you like traveling?
네, 여행하는 것을 아주 좋아해요.	[Yes! I really like traveling.]
아니요, 힘들어서 별로 안 좋아해요.	[No, it's exhausting, so I don't like it.]
저는 여행 하는 것에 관심이 없어요.	[I'm not interested in traveling.]
좋아하지만 여행을 거의 안 가요 .	[I like to travel, but I hardly ever do.]
좋지도 않지만 싫지도 않아요.	[I don't like it, but I also don't dislike it.]

Your Turn:

어디로 여행을 가요?	Where do you usually travel to?
주로 바다에 가서 호텔에 머물어요.	[I usually go to the beach and stay at a hotel.]
친구들이랑 종종 자동차 여행을 가요.	[I go on road trips with my friends now and then.]
자주 혼자서 다른 도시로 여행을 가요.	[I travel solo to other cities often.]
이번 여름에 한국에 갈 거예요.	[I'm going to Korea this summer.]
제주도 여행을 자주 가요.	[I travel to Jeju Island often.]

Your Turn:

육하원칙

여행하는 것을 좋아하세요?
[yeo-haeng-ha-neun geo-seul jo-a-ha-se-yo?]

Developing Your Answer

언제 여행을 가요?	When do you travel?
여름에는 주로 해외 여행을 가요.	[In summer I usually travel abroad.]
봄 방학에 하와이에 갔다올 거예요.	[I'm going to Hawaii for spring break.]
휴가 때 유럽에 갈 거예요.	[I'm going to Europe during my break.]
일 때문에 자주 출장을 가요.	[I often take business trips for work.]
주말에 당일치기로 여행을 가요.	[I take day trips on the weekend.]

Your Turn:

여행할 때 뭐 해요?	What do you do when you travel?
저는 가족하고 같이 해변에 가요.	[I go to the beach with my family.]
미술관하고 박물관을 방문해요.	[I visit art galleries and museums.]
맛있는 현지 음식을 많이 먹어 봐요.	[I try lots of delicious local foods.]
유명한 관광지를 구경해요.	[I look around famous tourist spots.]
휴양지에 가서 쉬는 것을 좋아해요.	[I like relaxing at tropical resorts.]

Your Turn:

쓰기

여행하는 것을 좋아하세요?
[yeo-haeng-ha-neun geo-seul jo-a-ha-se-yo?]

Try Writing Your Own Answer

1) Write your own answer below to the question   -- 여행하는 것을 좋아하세요? --

2) Get your answer corrected and rewrite your corrected answer here:

You can post your writing on an app/website like *Hellotalk* or *Hinative* for free corrections.

대화

여행하는 것을 좋아하세요?
[yeo-haeng-ha-neun geo-seul jo-a-ha-se-yo?]

Example Conversation

하린: 서아씨, 여행하는 것을 좋아하세요?
Seo-Ah, do you like traveling?

서아: 네! 사실 작년에 친구랑 제주도에 갔어요. 정말 재미있었어요.
Yes! Actually last year I went with my friend to Jeju Island. It was really fun.

하린: 저는 제주도에 가 본 적이 없어요. 제주도에서 뭘 했어요?
I haven't been to Jeju Island. What did you do in Jeju?

서아: 성산일출봉에서 산책하고 맛있**는** 제주흑돼지를 먹고 협재해수욕장에서 예**쁜** 노을을 봤어요.
I took a walk at Seongsan Ilchulbong Peak, ate delicious Jeju black pork, and saw the beautiful sunset at Hyeopjae Beach.

하린: 정말 재밌었겠네요.
That sounds like it was a lot of fun.

서아: 네, 다시 가고 싶어요. 다음에는 한라산에서 등산도 할 수 있으면 좋겠어요.
Yes, I want to go again. I hope I can hike Mt. Halla next time.

하리: 멋**진** 여행이었겠네요. 완전 제대로 여행했네요. 하하
You must have had a great trip. You really traveled right. Haha.

문화

여행하는 것을 좋아하세요?
[yeo-haeng-ha-neun geo-seul jo-a-ha-se-yo?]

Culture Note

제주도

Jeju Island (제주도), "the Hawaii of Korea," is located about 50 miles (80km) south of the Korean peninsula. It is a volcanic island and the largest island in Korea. It is a popular tourist destination, known for it's beautiful beaches, warm weather, and tall mountains, including the famous Mt. Halla (한라산).

The language of Jeju, Jejuan (known in Korea as 제주어), is a Korean dialect, though Korean and Jejuan are not mutually understandable. Jejuan was designated an endangered language by UNESCO in 2010. It currently has fewer than 10,000 native speakers, most of which are over the age of 75. [15]

Jeju boasts a number of famous local dishes, including an abundance of fresh seafood, and pork from the native black pig (제주흑돼지).

Jeju is also home to the hae-nyeo (해녀), the famous female divers who dive as far as 66 feet (20 meters) underwater without the aid of breathing apparatuses to collect abalone, conch, and seaweed. [16]

Q7

보통 건강을 위해 뭘 하세요?

[bo-tong geon-gan-geul wi-hae mwol ha-se-yo?]
What do you usually do for your health?

보통	: usually; normally; ordinarily
건강	: health
~을/를 위해	: for the sake of something
뭐 + ~을/를	: what + object particle
하다	: to do
~(으)세요	: honorific present tense sentence ending

대답

보통 건강을 위해 뭘 하세요?

[bo-tong geon-gan-geul wi-hae mwol ha-se-yo?]

What do you usually do for your health?

보통 물을 많이 마셔요.

최근에 다이어트도 시작해서 음식도 건강히 먹고 있어요.

그리고 음악을 들으면서 운동해요.

I usually drink lots of water.

I also started a diet recently, so I'm eating healthy, too.

And I also work out while listening to music.

Answer Breakdown

Vocabulary	Grammar
Nouns	~을/를 Object Particle
보통 - usually; ordinarily, normally	Present Tense ~아/어요
물 - water	Time~에
최근 - recently	N~도
다이어트 - a diet	A/V~아/어서 N~(이)라서
음식 - food	A ~ㄴ/은/는 N
그리고 - And (sentence starter)	V~고 있다
음악 - music	그리고, 그래서 & 하지만
Action Verbs	V~(으)면서
마시다 - to drink	A~게/이/히
시작하다 - to start	
먹다 - to eat food	
듣다 - to listen; to hear	
운동을 하다 - to exercise; to work out	
Descriptive Verbs	
많다 - to be many/a lot	
건강하다 - to be healthy	

설명

Grammar Spotlight

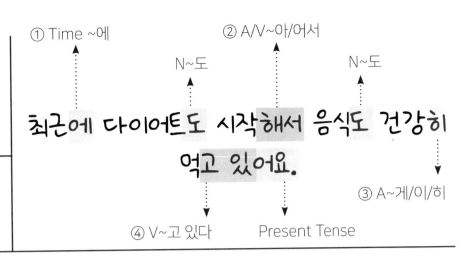

① Time ~에

N~도

② A/V~아/어서

N~도

최근에 다이어트도 시작해서 음식도 건강히 먹고 있어요.

③ A~게/이/히

④ V~고 있다

Present Tense

---

① Time~에: The particle ~에 is a prepositional particle, often aligning with the English meanings "in/at/on/to." When used with a time noun it marks it as the time "at" which some action occurs. The time noun "최근" (recently) is marked by **~에**, becoming "최근에..." (recently...)

최근**에** 살이 쪘어요.   I recently gained weight.

최근**에** 헬스장에 등록했어요.   Recently I joined a gym.

② A/V~아/어서: The form **~아/어서** attaches to the verb stem to connect two clauses. It is used when clause 1 of a sentence is the reason that clause 2 happens, and it means "so/since/because." In the example above, clause 1: "최근에 다이어트도 시작하다" (I also started a diet recently), becomes "최근에 다이어트도 시작**해서**..." (I also started a diet recently, so...)

최근에 살이 **쪄서** 헬스장에 등록했어요.   I gained weight recently, so I joined a gym.

건강한 몸을 만들고 싶**어서** 운동해요.   I exercise because I want a healthy body.

③ A~게/이/히: The form **~게/이/히** attaches to descriptive verbs, turning them into adverbs that can describe HOW a verb happens. Generally these are "-ly" words in English. We can attach **~히** to the verb "건강하다" (to be healthy) to make the adverb 건강**히** (healthily).

적당**히** 먹고 운동해서 건강한 편이에요.   I eat and work out right, so I'm pretty healthy.

충분**히** 자서 아침에 머리가 맑아요.   I get enough sleep, so my mind is clear in the morning.

④ V~고 있다: Attach **~고 있다** to an action verb stem in order to say that the action is currently in progress, either at the moment, or just generally happening in the present time. In the example above, the verb "먹다" (to eat) becomes "먹고 있어요" (I'm eating).

건강하게 음식을 **먹고 있어요.**   I'm eating healthy.

요즘 적당히 운동을 **하고 있어요.**   I'm getting the right amount of exercise these days.

문법

V~아/어 보다
[To talk about trying things]

Grammar Practice

V~아/어 보다
This form is used to talk about trying to do something, or trying something out (usually for the first time). Use **~아/어 봤다** to talk about something you tried in the past.

Scan the QR code to view a short grammar lesson PDF.

Given the English sentence below, use the grammar form above to write the equivalent expression in Korean. Including "저는" in your sentences is optional.

1. I tried doing yoga last year.

작년 - last year | 요가를 하다 - do yoga

2. I will try reading a Korean newspaper.

한국 신문 - Korean newspaper | 읽다 - read

3. I tried making a cake.

케이크 - cake | 만들다 - make

4. I tried listening to that song.

그 노래 - that song | *듣다 - listen

5. I tried bubble tea.

버블티 - bubble tea | 마시다 - to drink

*Irregular Verb: Be aware that this verb conjugates irregularly.

Please be aware that not all sentences have one exact translation, so answers may vary slightly.

어휘

보통 건강을 위해 뭘 하세요?
[bo-tong geon-gan-geul wi-hae mwol ha-se-yo?]

Recommended Vocabulary

보통 건강을 위해 뭘 해요? [What do you usually do for your health?]

운동을 하다 - to exercise	충분히 - enough	건강하다 - to be healthy
과자 - snacks	소금 - salt	설탕 - sugar
일찍 - early	요즘 - these days; lately	가볍다 - to be light
야채 - vegetables	과일 - fruits	고기 - meat
잠을 자다 - to sleep; to go to bed	비타민 - vitamins	다이어트를 하다 - to diet

다이어트를 해 봤어요? [Have you tried dieting?]

살이 찌다 - to gain weight	살이 빠지다 - to lose weight	적당히 - in moderation
간헐적 단식 - intermittent fasting	저탄고지 - a low-fat diet	원푸드 - a 'one food' diet
킬로그램 - kilograms	빼다 - to remove; get rid of	탄수화물 - carbs
식사량 조절 - portion control	음료수 - a drink; a beverage	제대로 - properly

어떤 운동을 해 봤어요? [What exercises have you tried?]

규칙적으로 - regularly	러닝을 하다 - to go running	전신운동 - full-body workout
복근 운동 - ab exercises	사이클을 타다 - to do cycling	요가를 하다 - to do yoga
근육 운동 - muscle building	조깅하다 - to go jogging	산책하다 - to go for a walk

운동을 왜 했어요? [Why did you try exercising?]

살을 빼다 - to reduce weight	몸을 만들다 - to bulk up	운동을 하다 - to exercise
시작하다 - to start	스트레스가 풀리다 - to relieve stress	스트레스를 받다 - to get stressed; to be stressed
유연하다 - flexible; limber	날씬하다 - slender; slim	습관 - a habit

77

육하원칙

보통 건강을 위해 뭘 하세요?
[bo-tong geon-gan-geul wi-hae mwol ha-se-yo?]

Developing Your Answer

보통 건강을 위해 뭘 해요?	What do you usually do for your health?
요즘 설탕하고 소금을 덜 먹고 있어요.	[Lately I'm eating less sugar and salt.]
일주일에 4번씩 가벼운 운동을 해요.	[I do some light exercise 4 times a week.]
보통 저녁에 조금만 먹어요.	[I usually only eat a little bit at dinner.]
일찍 자고 일찍 일어나려고 해요.	[I try to go to bed early, and get up early.]
하루에 1시간씩 운동해요.	[I work out for about an hour a day.]

Your Turn:

다이어트를 해 봤어요?	Have you tried dieting?
다이어트를 해 봤는데 살이 잘 안 빠졌어요.	[I tried dieting, but I didn't lose much weight.]
아니요, 보통 적당히 먹고 운동해요.	[No, I usually eat and work out in moderation.]
작년에 해 봤는데 10킬로그램을 뺐어요.	[I tried it last year, and I lost 10 kilograms.]
네, 간헐적 단식을 해 본 적이 있어요.	[Yes, I've tried intermittent fasting before.]
다이어트는 안 했지만 한번 해 보고 싶어요.	[I haven't dieted, but I'd like to give it a try once.]

Your Turn:

육하원칙

보통 건강을 위해 뭘 하세요?
[bo-tong geon-gan-geul wi-hae mwol ha-se-yo?]

Developing Your Answer

어떤 운동을 해 봤어요?	What exercises have you tried?
규칙적으로 러닝을 해요.	[I go running regularly.]
전신운동을 몇 번 해 봤어요.	[I've done a few full-body work outs.]
그냥 복근 운동을 해 봤어요.	[I just tried doing ab exercises.]
사이클을 자주 타고 요가도 해요.	[I often do cycling and yoga.]
등산하고 조깅을 해 봤어요.	[I've tried hiking and jogging.]

Your Turn:

운동을 왜 했어요?	Why did you try exercising?
살을 빼고 싶어서요.	[Because I wanted to lose weight.]
건강해지고 싶어서 했어요.	[I did it because I wanted to be healthy.]
몸을 만들고 싶어서 운동을 시작했어요.	[I wanted to bulk up, so I started exercising.]
스트레스가 풀려서 운동해 봤어요.	[I tried exercising because it relieves stress.]
건강하게 먹고 싶어서 다이어트를 했어요.	[I wanted to eat healthy, so I went on a diet.]

Your Turn:

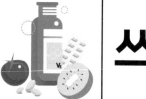

쓰기

1) Write your own answer below to the question   -- 보통 건강을 위해 뭘 하세요? --

2) Get your answer corrected and rewrite your corrected answer here:

You can post your writing on an app/website like *Hellotalk* or *Hinative* for free corrections.

대화

보통 건강을 위해 뭘 하세요?
[bo-tong geon-gan-geul wi-hae mwol ha-se-yo?]

Example Conversation

서준: 사라씨, 보통 건강하게 먹는 편이에요?

Sarah, do you usually tend to eat healthy?

사라: 글쎄요. 그럴 때도 있지만 그렇지 않을 때도 있어요. 서준씨는요?

I'm not sure. Sometimes I do, and sometimes I don't. How about you, Seojun?

서준: 아니요, 저는 먹고 싶은 걸 먹는 편이에요. 그렇지만 건강하게 먹고 싶어요.
다이어트를 **해 본** 적이 있어요?

No, I tend to eat whatever I want. But I do want to eat healthy. Have you ever dieted?

사라: 음, 저는 다이어트를 딱히 안 해요. 그냥 모든 것을 적당히 먹는 편이에요. 서준씨는요?

Hm, I don't really do a diet exactly. I just eat everything in moderation. You?

서준: 저는 많이 **해 봤어요**. 간헐적 단식, 저탄고지, 원푸드...

I've tried so many. Intermittent fasting, low-fat, one-food...

사라: 아, 그렇군요. 좀 많네요. 하하

Ah, I see. That's quite a lot. Haha

서준: 네... 너무 많죠... 그냥 마음대로 먹고 싶어요...

Yes... too many... I just want to eat whatever I want...

사라: 너무 걱정하지 마세요. 그냥 적당히 먹고 적당히 운동하면 돼요.

Don't worry too much. If you just eat and exercise in moderation, it'll be fine.

문화

보통 건강을 위해 뭘 하세요?
[bo-tong geon-gan-geul wi-hae mwol ha-se-yo?]

Culture Note

다이어트

In Korean, the word "다이어트" has been derived from the English word, "diet." However, as can sometimes happen with loanwords that have been adopted into Korean, it has changed slightly from it's original English meaning. While we think of "diet" referring only to food consumption, the Korean term "다이어트" is used to refer to any and all methods used to lose weight, including food, exercise, and even medical procedures.

Traditionally, the Korean diet predominantly consisted of rice and vegetables. [20] But in modern times, many factors such as changes in eating habits (e.g. eating more meat, dairy, and processed foods), a more sedentary lifestyle, and unrealistic beauty standards in the media have produced a strong interest in dieting and weight loss in Korea.

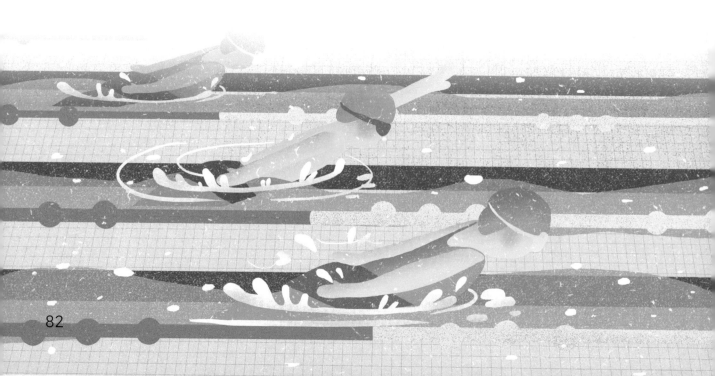

Q8

한국에 가 본 적이 있나요?

[han-gu-ge ga-bon jeo-gi in-na-yo?]

Have you ever been to Korea?

한국 : Korea

~에 : location of motion/existence particle

가다 : to go

V~아/어 보다 : to try doing some verb

V~(으)ㄴ 적이 있다 : to have experienced doing some verb

V~나요? : an ending used to make a question less direct

대답

한국에 가 본 적이 있나요?

[han-gu-ge ga-bon jeo-gi in-na-yo?]

Have you ever been to Korea?

네, 작년에 서울에 갔어요.
서울에 갔을 때 맛있는 음식을 먹어 봤어요.
그리고 한복도 입어 봤어요!

- -

Yes, I went to Seoul last year.
When I went to Seoul, I tried delicious foods.
And I also tried on a hanbok!

Answer Breakdown

Vocabulary	Grammar
Nouns	~을/를 Object Particle
네 - yes	Time~에 V
작년 - last year	Place~에 가다/오다
서울 - Seoul	A/V~았/었다 Past Tense
음식 - food	N~도
그리고: And (sentence starter)	A~ㄴ/은/는 N
한복 - hanbok (traditional Korean clothing)	그리고, 그래서 & 하지만
Action Verbs	A/V~ㄹ/을 때, N 때
가다 - to go	V~아/어 보다
먹다 - to eat	
입다 - to wear	
Descriptive Verbs	
맛있다 - to be delicious	

The grammar is color-coded to match chapters in *Conversational Korean Grammar*.

설명

Grammar Spotlight

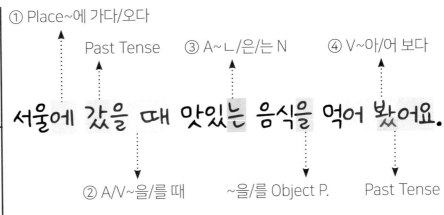

① Place~에 가다/오다

Past Tense

③ A~ㄴ/은/는 N

④ V~아/어 보다

서울에 갔을 때 맛있는 음식을 먹어 봤어요.

② A/V~을/를 때

~을/를 Object P.

Past Tense

---

① PLACE~에 가다: The location particle **~에** attaches to a place noun, and can be followed by the motion verb "가다" (to go). It means "I go to (place)." The sentence above uses "서울**에** 가다" (I go to Seoul).

매년 서울**에** 갔어요.	I went to Seoul every year.
내년에 부산**에** 갈 거예요.	I'm going to Busan next year.

② A/V~ㄹ/을 때: The form **~ㄹ/을 때** attaches to the stem of action verbs and descriptive verbs, and it means "the time that" or "when" that verb happens. As in the sentence above, the past tense form **~았/었을 때** can also be used. In this case "서울**에** 가다" (I go to Seoul) becomes "서울에 **갔을때...**" (when I went to Seoul...)

부산에 갔**을 때** 해운대에 갔어요.	I went to Haeundae when I went to Busan.
전주에 갔**을 때** 한옥 마을에 갔어요.	When I went to Jeonju I went to a traditional village.

③ A~ㄴ/은/는 N: Attach **~ㄴ/은/는** to a descriptive verb stem to change it into an adjective. Then, place it in front of a noun to describe it. Use **~ㄴ** when the stem ends in a vowel, use **~은** when the stem ends in a consonant, and use **~는** when the stem ends in 있다/없다. In the example above, "맛있다" (to be delicious) becomes "맛있**는** 음식" (delicious food).

광주에 갔을 때 맛있**는** 음식을 먹었어요.	I ate delicious food when I went to Gwangju.
제주도에 갔을 때 신선**한** 해산물을 먹었어요.	I ate fresh seafood when I went to Jeju Island.

④ V~아/어 보다: Attach **~아/어 보다** to an action verb stem to say that you try doing that verb. When used with the past tense, the form **~아/어 봤다** can be used to say "I tried". In the example above "먹다" (to eat) becomes "먹**어 봤어요**" (I tried eating).

한국에 갔을 때 매운 떡볶이를 먹**어 봤어요**.	I tried spicy tteokbokki when I went to korea.
서울에서 역사적인 장소에 많이 가 **봤어요**.	I went to lots of historic places in Seoul.

문법

V~(으)ㄴ 적이 있다/없다
[For talking about your life experiences]

Grammar Practice

V~(으)ㄴ 적이 있다/없다

Use this form to talk about things you have or haven't done before. Use ~(으)ㄴ 적이 있다 to say "(subject) has done" and ~(으)ㄴ 적이 없다 to say "(subject) hasn't done."

Scan the QR code to view a short grammar lesson PDF.

Given the English sentence below, use the grammar form above to write the equivalent expression in Korean. Including "저는" in your sentences is optional.

1. I haven't gone on a trip on my birthday.   생일 - birthday | 여행을 가다 - go on a trip

....

2. I haven't exercised at a gym before.   헬스장 - gym | 운동하다 - to exercise

....

3. I have been hospitalized before.   입원하다 - to be hospitalized

....

4. I haven't tried eating kimchi before.   김치 - kimchi | 먹다 - to eat

....

5. I have watched a Korean drama.   한국 드라마 - Korean drama | 보다 - to watch

....

Please be aware that not all sentences have one exact translation, so answers may vary slightly.

어휘

한국에 가 본 적이 있나요?
[han-gu-ge ga-bon jeo-gi in-na-yo?]

Recommended Vocabulary

한국에 가 본 적이 있나요? [Have you ever been to Korea?]

몇 년 전 - a few years ago	작년 - last year	올해 - this year
내년 - next year	아직 - yet; still	다시 - again
가을 - autumn; fall	겨울 - winter	봄 - spring
여름 - summer	일주일 동안 - for a week	재미있다 - fun; interesting

한국에서 어디를 갈 수 있어요? [Where can you go in Korea?]

경복궁 - Gyeongbok Palace	설악산 - Mt. Seorak	부산 - Busan
해운대 해수욕장 - Haeundae Beach	등산하다 - to hike	한옥 마을 - a village of traditional Korean houses
강남 - Gangnam	제주도 - Jeju Island	홍대 - Hongdae
한강 - the Han River	맛집 - a popular restaurant	서울 - Seoul
투어하다 - to tour	등산하다 - to hike	방문하다 - to visit

한국에 가는 이유가 뭐예요? [What are the reasons people go to Korea?]

문화 - culture	역사적이다 - to be historic	경험하다 - to experience
연습하다 - to practice	얘기하다 - to talk/chat (with)	현지 한식 - local Korean food
먹어 보다 - to try (eating)	장소 - a place	벚꽃 - cherry blossoms

한국에서 뭘 할 수 있어요? [What can you do in Korea?]

자전거 - a bicycle	타다 - to ride	찜질방 - a Korean public spa
기념품- a souvenir	길거리 음식 - street food	사우나 - a sauna
전통- tradition	시장 - a market	관광지 - sights; attractions
즐기다 - to enjoy	놀이공원 - a theme park	체험 - an experience

한국에 가 본 적이 있나요?
[han-gu-ge ga-bon jeo-gi in-na-yo?]

Developing Your Answer

한국에 가 본 적이 있나요?	Have you ever been to Korea?
네, 작년에 한국에 가 봤어요.	[Yes, I went to Korea last year.]
아니요, 한국에 가 본 적이 없어요.	[No, I've never been to Korea.]
올해 한국에 갈 거예요.	[I'm going to Korea this year.]
가 본 적은 없지만 가고 싶어요.	[I haven't been, but I want to go.]
네, 한국 여행을 갔는데 재밌었어요.	[Yes, I traveled to Korea, and it was fun.]

Your Turn:

한국에서 어디를 갈 수 있어요?	Where can you go in Korea?
서울에 있는 경복궁에 가 봤어요.	[I went to Gyeongbokgung in Seoul.]
친구들하고 설악산을 등산했어요.	[I climbed Mt. Seorak with my friends.]
부산 해운대 해수욕장에 갔어요.	[I went to Haeundae Beach in Busan.]
전주 한옥 마을을 방문했어요.	[I visited the traditional village in Jeonju.]
강남 맛집을 투어했어요.	[I toured the popular restaurants in Gangnam.]

Your Turn:

육하원칙

한국에 가 본 적이 있나요?
[han-gu-ge ga-bon jeo-gi in-na-yo?]

Developing Your Answer

한국에 가는 이유가 뭐예요?	What are the reasons people go to Korea?
한국 문화를 경험하고 싶어서요.	[I want to experience Korean culture.]
한국어를 연습하고 싶어요.	[I want to practice Korean.]
한국 사람하고 얘기해 보고 싶어요.	[I want to try talking with Korean people.]
현지 한식을 먹어 볼 수 있어요.	[You can try local Korean foods.]
역사적인 장소를 방문할 수 있어요.	[You can visit historic places.]

Your Turn:

한국에서 뭘 할 수 있어요?	What can you do in Korea?
한강에서 자전거를 탈 수 있어요.	[You can ride bikes at the Han River.]
찜질방에서 사우나를 즐겨요.	[I enjoy the sauna at a Korean spa.]
한국 문화 체험을 해 볼 수 있어요.	[You can experience Korean culture.]
길거리 음식을 먹어 볼 수있어요.	[You can try street foods.]
전통 시장에 갈 수 있어요.	[You can go to traditional markets.]

Your Turn:

쓰기

한국에 가 본 적이 있나요?
[han-gu-ge ga-bon jeo-gi in-na-yo?]

Try Writing Your Own Answer

1) Write your own answer below to the question -- 한국에 가 본 적이 있나요? --

_____

_____

_____

_____

_____

_____

2) Get your answer corrected and rewrite your corrected answer here:

_____

_____

_____

_____

_____

_____

_____

You can post your writing on an app/website like _Hellotalk_ or _Hinative_ for free corrections.

대화 한국에 가 본 적이 있나요?
[han-gu-ge ga-bon jeo-gi in-na-yo?]

Example Conversation

사라: 소피씨, 한국에 가 **본 적이 있어요**?
Sophie, have you ever been to Korea?

소피: 네, 작년에 갔어요. 사라씨는요?
Yes, I went last year. How about you, Sarah?

사라: 저는 아직 가 **본 적이 없어요**. 소피 씨의 한국 여행은 어땠어요?
I still haven't ever been. How was your Korea trip, Sophie?

소피: 정말 좋았어요. 서울에 갔는데 유명한 관광지에 갔고 맛있는 음식을 많이 먹었어요!
It was really great. I went to Seoul, so I visited famous sites, and had lots of tasty food!

사라: 우와, 좋겠네요! 저도 한국에 가고 싶어요. 만약 서울에 간다면, 뭘 하는 걸 추천해요?
Wow, that sounds great! I want to go to Korea too. If I had the chance to go to Seoul, what would you recommend doing?

소피: 음... 아마 경복궁이요! 한복을 입으면 무료로 입장하고 예쁜 사진을 찍을 수 있어요!
Hm... maybe Gyeonbokgung! If you wear a hanbok you get in free, and you can take pretty pictures!

사라: 와, 고마워요! 올해 꼭 가고 싶어요.
Wow, thank you! I definitely want to go this year.

문화

한국에 가 본 적이 있나요?
[han-gu-ge ga-bon jeo-gi in-na-yo?]

Culture Note

경복궁

Gyeongbok Palace (경복궁) was built in 1395 at the beginning of the Joseon Dynasty in what is now northern Seoul. It is the largest of the five grand palaces built in Seoul, and was the residence of the kings, their households, and the government of Joseon. [1]

경복궁 has been subjected to many instances of destruction including the Japanese occupation of Korea in the early 1900s, and the Korean War in 1950. The South Korean government began rebuilding the palace in 1989, and though 경복궁 is open to the public, the restoration remains ongoing.

Today tourists can rent traditional Korean clothing called hanbok (한복) to wear while touring the palace, as well as watch the hourly changing of the royal guards. It is also possible to taste royal food and watch traditional performances. 경복궁 is even occasionally open for night tours, where visitors can walk the palace grounds after dark and take beautiful pictures of the palace lit up at night.

가장 싫어하는 집안일은 무엇인가요?

[ga-jang shi-reo-ha-neun ji-ba-ni-reun mu-eo-shin-ga-yo?]

What chore do you hate the most?

가장 : the most	
싫어하다 : to dislike; to hate	
V~는 N : present tense noun-modifying (adjective) form	
집안일 : housework; household chores	
~은/는 : topic particle	
무엇 : what	
N~인가요? : an ending used to make a question less direct	

대답

가장 싫어하는 집안일은 무엇인가요?

[ga-jang shi-reo-ha-neun ji-ba-ni-reun mu-eo-shin-ga-yo?]

What chore do you hate the most?

가장 싫어하는 집안일은 설거지예요.

설거지를 할 때 너무 심심해요.

그래서 항상 설거지하면서 음악을 듣는 것을 선호해요.

The chore I hate the most is doing the dishes.
When I do the dishes I'm so bored.
That's why I always prefer listening to music while I do the dishes.

Answer Breakdown

Vocabulary	Grammar
Nouns	~은/는 Topic Particle
가장 - most; best	~을/를 Object Particle
집안일 - housework; chores	N~이에요/예요
설거지 - dish washing; washing the dishes	Present Tense ~아/어요
너무 - really, very, so, too much	V~는 것
그래서 - so; therefore; that's why	그리고, 그래서 & 하지만
항상 - always	Words of Frequency
음악 - music	가장 & 제일
Action Verbs	V~는 N
싫어하다 - to dislike; to hate	A/V~ㄹ/을 때, N 때
설거지를 하다 - to do the dishes	V~(으)면서, N(이)면서
듣다 - to listen; to hear	
선호하다 - to prefer	
Descriptive Verbs	
심심하다 - to be bored	

The grammar is color-coded to match chapters in *Conversational Korean Grammar*.

설명

Grammar Spotlight

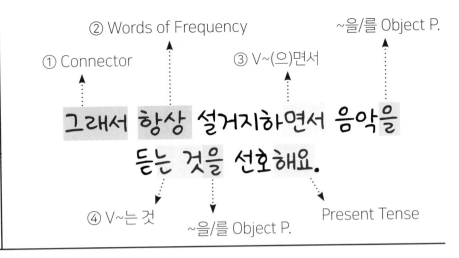

① Connector

② Words of Frequency

③ V~(으)면서

~을/를 Object P.

그래서 항상 설거지하면서 음악을 듣는 것을 선호해요.

④ V~는 것

~을/를 Object P.

Present Tense

① Sentence Connector 그래서: The word **그래서** (so, therefore) is one of many "sentence connectors." These words always come after a period, beginning a new sentence and linking the two sentences together. **그래서** is used when the preceding sentence is the reason that the next sentence happens.

그래서 저는 빨래 개기를 싫어해요.   That's why I hate folding the laundry.
그래서 정리하는 건 너무 귀찮아요.   So tidying up is such a hassle.

② Words of Frequency 항상: The word **항상** (always) is one of many "frequency words" that are used to talk about how often an action is done or a situation occurs. In the example above, the speaker doesn't just prefer this situation, they **always** prefer it.

항상 정리하면서 요리해요.   I always tidy up while I cook.
가끔 드라마를 보면서 빨래를 개요. I sometimes watch dramas while folding the laundry.

③ V~(으)면서: ~(으)면서 attaches to action verb stems, and is used when you want to talk about two actions occurring at the same time. It often translates to "while." The sentence above combines the actions "설거지하다" (to do the dishes) and 음악을 듣다 (to listen to music) using **~(으)면서**, making "설거지하**면서** 음악을 들어요" (while I do the dishes, I listen to music.)

욕실 청소를 하**면서** 노래를 불러요.   I sing while cleaning the bathroom.
바닥을 쓸**면서** 춤을 춰요.   I dance while I sweep the floor.

④ V~는 것: Attach **~는 것** to the verb stem of an action verb to use it as a noun in your sentence. The verb used above "듣다" (to listen) becomes the noun "듣**는 것**" (listening). You can now talk about the characteristics/state of "listening" as you would any other noun.

집안일 하**는 것**은 항상 지루해요.   Doing house chores is always boring.
빨래하**는 것**은 거의 남편의 일이에요. Doing the laundry is almost always my husband's job.

문법

V~(으)면서
[To talk about simultaneous actions]

Grammar Practice

V~(으)면서
Use this form to talk about two action verbs being done at the same time. Attach **~으면서** when the verb stem ends in a consonant, and **~면서** when it ends in a vowel.

Scan the QR code to view a short grammar lesson PDF.

Given the English sentence below, use the grammar form above to write the equivalent expression in Korean. Including "저는" in your sentences is optional.

1. I watch TV while I eat dinner.
   저녁 - dinner | 먹다 - eat | 텔레비전 - TV

....

2. I listen to music while I exercise.
   운동하다 - exercise | 음악 - music | *듣다 - listen

....

3. I read a book while I wait for the bus.
   버스 - bus | 기다리다 - wait | 읽다 - read

....

4. I ate a snack while I did my homework.
   숙제를 하다 - do homework | 과자 - snack

....

5. While I clean I watch Netflix.
   청소하다 - to clean | 넷플릭스 - Netflix

....

*Irregular Verb: Be aware that this verb conjugates irregularly.

ANSWERS: 1. 저녁을 먹으면서 텔레비전을 봐요. 2. 운동하면서 음악을 들어요. 3. 버스를 기다리면서 책을 읽어요. 4. 숙제를 하면서 과자를 먹었어요. 5. 청소하면서 넷플릭스를 봐요.

Please be aware that not all sentences have one exact translation, so answers may vary slightly.

어휘

가장 싫어하는 집안일은 무엇인가요?
[ga-jang shi-reo-ha-neun ji-ba-ni-reun mu-eo-shin-ga-yo?]

Recommended Vocabulary

가장 싫어하는 집안일은 뭐예요? [What chore do you hate the most?]

걸레질을 하다 - to mop the floor

빨래하다 - to do laundry

정리하다 - to organize/tidy

빨래를 개다 - to fold laundry

씻다 - to wash/rinse

청소기 - a vacuum cleaner

손으로 - by hand

잔디를 깎다 - to mow the lawn

설거지를 하다 - to do dishes

치우다 - to put/clear away

청소기를 돌리다 - to vacuum

쓰다 - to use

세탁기 - a washing machine

집안일 - house chores

물을 주다 - to give water; to water sth (e.g. a plant)

청소하다 - to clean

닦다 - to wipe

바닥을 쓸다 - to sweep

대걸레로 닦다 - to mop

산책시키다 - to walk (a pet)

요리하다 - to cook

어떤 집안일을 해요? [What chores do you do?]

화장실 - bathroom

바닥 - the floor

책상 - a desk

부엌 - kitchen

거실 - living room

거울 - a mirror

방 - room

집 - house/home

그릇 - bowls/plates/dishes

집안 일을 언제해요? [When do you do your chores?]

더럽다 - to be dirty

저녁 - evening; dinner

매일 - every day

주말 - weekend

봄 - spring

시간이 있다 - to have time

아침 - morning; breakfast

밤 - night

매년 - every year

집안일을 왜 싫어해요? [Why do you hate your chores?]

재미없다 - boring; not fun

힘들다 - difficult; hard; tiring

귀찮다 - to be a hassle/pain

시간이 걸리다 - to take time

아프다 - to be hurt/sick

싫다 - to be bad; unlikeable

시끄럽다 - to be loud/noisy

냄새가 나다 - to smell/stink

어렵다 - to be difficult/hard

육하원칙

가장 싫어하는 집안일은 무엇인가요?
[ga-jang shi-reo-ha-neun ji-ba-ni-reun mu-eo-shin-ga-yo?]

Developing Your Answer

가장 싫어하는 집안일은 뭐예요?	What chore do you hate the most?
화장실 청소하는 걸 가장 싫어해요.	[I hate cleaning the bathroom the most.]
가장 싫어하는 집안일은 설거지예요.	[The chore I hate most is doing the dishes.]
빨래를 개는 게 최악이에요.	[Folding the laundry is the worst.]
청소기 돌리는 걸 정말 싫어해요.	[I really hate vacuuming.]
방 정리를 가장 싫어해요.	[I hate cleaning my room the most.]

Your Turn:

어떤 집안일을 해요?	What chores do you do?
화장실에서 거울을 닦아요.	[I clean the mirror in the bathroom.]
부엌에서 설거지하고 그릇을 치워요.	[In the kitchen I do the dishes and put them away.]
책상을 깨끗이 정리해요.	[I organize my desk neatly.]
거실에서 청소기를 돌려요.	[I vacuum in the living room.]
집에서 바닥을 쓸고 대걸레로 닦아요.	[I sweep and mop the floors at home.]

Your Turn:

육하원칙

가장 싫어하는 집안일은 무엇인가요?
[ga-jang shi-reo-ha-neun ji-ba-ni-reun mu-eo-shin-ga-yo?]

Developing Your Answer

집안 일을 언제 해요?	When do you do your chores?
매년 봄에 집 전체를 청소해요.	[I clean the whole house every spring.]
주말에는 화장실하고 부엌을 청소해요.	[I clean my bathroom and kitchen on the weekend.]
엄청 더러울 때 화장실을 청소해요.	[I clean the bathroom when it's really dirty.]
시간이 있을 때 설거지를 하는 편이에요.	[I tend to do the dishes when I have time.]
매일 식사 준비를 해요.	[I prepare meals every day.]

Your Turn:

집안일을 왜 싫어해요?	Why do you hate your chores?
청소기 돌리는 건 귀찮아서 싫어요.	[I don't like vacuuming because it's a hassle.]
설거지가 너무 힘들어요.	[Doing the dishes is so exhausting.]
바닥을 쓸면 허리가 아파요.	[My back hurts when I sweep the floor.]
화장실에서 냄새가 나서 청소가 싫어요.	[The bathroom smells, so I hate cleaning it.]
이불 세탁은 시간이 많이 걸려서 싫어요.	[Washing blankets takes a lot of time, so I hate it.]

Your Turn:

쓰기

가장 싫어하는 집안일은 무엇인가요?
[ga-jang shi-reo-ha-neun ji-ba-ni-reun mu-eo-shin-ga-yo?]

Try Writing Your Own Answer

1) Write your own answer below to the question   -- 가장 싫어하는 집안일은 무엇인가요? --

2) Get your answer corrected and rewrite your corrected answer here:

대화

가장 싫어하는 집안일은 무엇인가요?
[ga-jang shi-reo-ha-neun ji-ba-ni-reun mu-eo-shin-ga-yo?]

Example Conversation

지호: 토니씨, 어렸을 때 집안일을 해야 했어요?

Tony, did you have to do chores when you were young?

토니: 네, 저는 매일 정원에 물을 주고 개를 산책시켜야 했어요. 그래도 개를 산책시키**면서** 노래를 듣는 건 재미있었던 것 같아요. 지호씨는요?

Yes, I had to water the plants and walk the dog every day. But still, I think it was fun listening to music while I walked the dog. What about you, Jiho?

지호: 네, 밥 먹은 다음에 음식물 쓰레기 담당이었어요. 너무 싫었어요.

Yes, after eating I was responsible for the food waste. I really hated it.

토니: 아, 진짜요? 왜 그렇게 싫어했어요?

Oh, really? Why did you hate it so much?

지호: 음식물 쓰레기 냄새가 고약하고 음식물 쓰레기통도 더럽잖아요.

Because food waste is disgusting, and the food waste bin is gross too.

토니: 아 그렇죠. 어렸을 때 우리 집에는 디스포저가 있어서 음식물 쓰레기를 거의 다 싱크대로 버리기만 하면 됐어요.

Oh, I see. When I was a kid, there was a garbage disposal at my house, so almost all the food waste could just go down the sink.

지호: 아, 그럼 편하겠지만 그런식으로 하면 음식물 쓰레기를 재활용할 수 없어요.

Oh, that sounds convenient, but if you do that you can't recycle your food waste.

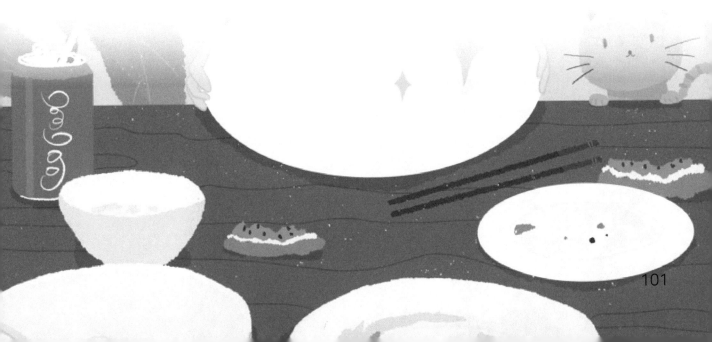

가장 싫어하는 집안일은 무엇인가요?
[ga-jang shi-reo-ha-neun ji-ba-ni-reun mu-eo-shin-ga-yo?]

Culture Note

음식물 쓰레기

Korean meals are typically accompanied by lots of small side-dishes called banchan (반찬), but these side-dishes are often left unfinished and end up needing to be thrown away at the end of a meal. However, simply throwing away food waste with the rest of the general trash is actually illegal in Korea.

Instead, each household has a small bin usually kept near the kitchen sink. Households place their food waste in these bins and then deposit the food waste in a designated collection area at their building complex. The food waste is then collected by trucks and taken for processing. Processing plants squeeze out the moisture and turn that moisture into bio gas and bio oil, while the dry waste is turned into fertilizer and animal feed. In this way, Korea now processes about 95% of it's food waste [2].

Q10

제일 좋아하는 명절은 뭐예요?

[je-il jo-a-ha-neun myeong-jeo-reun mwo-e-yo?]

What's your favorite holiday?

제일	: most; best
좋아하다	: to like
V~는 N	: present tense noun-modifying (adjective) form
명절	: a holiday
~은/는	: topic particle
뭐	: what
~이에요/예요	: the copula "to be"

대답

저는 추석을 제일 좋아해요.

회사에 가지 않고 명절 음식을 많이 먹을 수 있어서 좋아요.

한국인이지만 할로윈도 좋아해요.

- -

My favorite holiday is Chuseok.
It's great because I don't go to work, and I can eat a lot of holiday foods.
I'm Korean, but I also like Halloween.

Answer Breakdown

Vocabulary	Grammar
Nouns	~은/는 Topic Particle
저 - I; me	~을/를 Object Particle
추석 - the Korean autumn/harvest holiday	Present Tense ~아/어요
제일 - most; best	Place~에 가다/오다
회사 - work; the office	A/V~지 않다
명절 음식 - holiday food(s)	N~도
한국인 - a Korean person; a Korean	A/V~고, N~(이)고
할로윈 - Halloween	A/V~아/어서, N~(이)라서
Action Verbs	A/V~지만, N~(이)지만
좋아하다 - to like	가장 & 제일
가다 - to go	V~(으)ㄹ 수 있다/없다
먹다 - to eat	A~게/이/히
Descriptive Verbs	
많다 - to be a lot/many	
좋다 - to be good; likeable	

The grammar is color-coded to match chapters in *Conversational Korean Grammar.*

설명

Grammar Spotlight

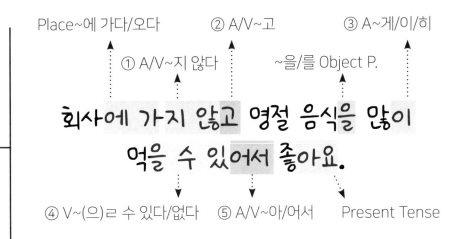

Place~에 가다/오다
② A/V~고
③ A~게/이/히
① A/V~지 않다
~을/를 Object P.

회사에 가지 않고 영절 음식을 많이 억을 수 있어서 좋아요.

④ V~(으)ㄹ 수 있다/없다　　⑤ A/V~아/어서　　Present Tense

---

① A/V~지 않다: When attached to the verb stem of a verb, **~지 않다** negates that verb. In the example above, the verb "가다"(to go) becomes "가**지 않다**" (to not go).

크리스마스에는 회사에 가**지 않아요**.　　You don't go to the office on Christmas.

추석에는 떡국을 먹**지 않아요**.　　You don't eat tteokguk on Chuseok.

② A/V~고: The form **~고** attaches to a verb stem to connect two clauses in a sentence together, and means "and". In the sentence above we have "회사에 가지 않다" (to not go to the office), which becomes "회사에 가지 않**고**..." (I don't go to the office and...)

명절 때 보통 요리하지 않**고** 먹는 편이에요.　On holidays I usually don't cook; I just eat.

명절에는 아무것도 하지 않**고** 쉬는 편이에요. I don't do anything on holidays; I just relax.

③ A~게/이/히: You can attach **게/이/히** to descriptive verbs to turn them into adverbs. The verb "많다" means "to be many" and you can attach **~이** to make the adverb 많**이** ("many").

성탄절에는 트리를 예쁘**게** 꾸미고 조명도 달아요.　On Christmas we decorate the tree, and hang lights.

설날에는 한복을 입고 세뱃돈을 넉넉**히** 받아요.　On Seollal I wear a hanbok and get lots of pocket money.

④ V~(으)ㄹ 수 있다: This form is used to talk about ability. Attach **~(으)ㄹ 수 있다** to talk about actions you can do. In the example above, "먹다"(to eat) becomes "먹**을 수 있어요**." (I can eat.)

할로윈에는 사탕을 많이 받**을 수 있어요**.　You can get lots of candy on Halloween.

어린이날에는 재밌게 놀 **수 있어요**.　On Children's Day you can have a lot of fun.

⑤ A/V~아/어서: Use **~아/어서** to join two clauses with the meaning of "so/because/since." In the example above "명절 음식을 많이 먹을 수 있다" (to be able to eat lots of holiday food) becomes　"명절 음식을 많이 먹을 수 있**어서**..." (I can eat lots of holiday food, so...)

선물을 많이 받을 수 있**어서** 성탄절을 좋아해요. I like Christmas because I can get a lot of presents.

명절에는 쉴 수 있**어서** 좋아요.　　　　　Holidays are great because I can rest.

문법

V~고 싶다
[To talk about things you want to do]

Grammar Practice

V~고 싶다

Attach this form to the stem of an action verb to say "I want to (do)" that verb. Use the form **~고 싶었다** to talk about things you wanted to do in the past.

Scan the QR code to view a short grammar lesson PDF.

Given the English sentence below, use the grammar form above to write the equivalent expression in Korean. Including "저는" in your sentences is optional.

1. I want to live in Korea next year.　　　내년 - next year | 한국 - Korea | 살다 - live

....

2. I want to eat dinner at a restaurant.　　식당 - restaurant | 저녁 - dinner | 먹다 - eat

....

3. I wanted to read a book at home.　　　집 - home | 책 - book | 읽다 - read

....

4. I wanted to try skiing in America.　　　미국 - America | 스키를 타다 - to ski

....

5. I want to sleep, but I can't now.　　　자다 - sleep | 지금 - now

....

ANSWERS: 1. 내년에 한국에(서) 살고 싶어요. 2. 식당에서 저녁을 먹고 싶어요. 3. 집에서 책을 읽고 싶었어요. 4. 미국에서 스키를 타고 싶었어요. 5. 지금 자고 싶은데 잘 수 없어요./잠 잘 수 없어요.

Please be aware that not all sentences have one exact translation, so answers may vary slightly.

어휘

제일 좋아하는 명절은 뭐예요?
[je-il jo-a-ha-neun myeong-jeo-reun mwo-e-yo?]

Recommended Vocabulary

제일 좋아하는 명절은 뭐예요? [What's your favorite holiday?]

설날- Seollal (Lunar New Year's Day)

추석 - Chuseok (Korean mid-autumn holiday)

발렌타인 데이 - Valentine's Day

어린이날 - Children's Day

부활절 - Easter

하누카 - Hanukkah

콴자 - Kwanzaa

새해 - New Years Day

라마단 - Ramadan

홀리- Holi

할로윈 - Halloween

한글날 - Hangul Day

크리스마스/성탄절 - Christ-mas

부처님 오신 날 - Buddha's Birthday

명절 - a national holiday

누구하고 같이 명절을 축하해요? [Who do you celebrate the holidays with?]

가족 - family

친구 - a friend

혼자(서) - alone; by oneself

친척 - a relative

애인 - a partner; a lover

아이 - a kid; a child

축하하다 - to celebrate

보내나 - '1) to send 2) to spend (time)

부모님 - parents

명절을 어떻게 보내요? [How do you spend the holidays?]

요리하다 - to cook

놀다 - to play; hang out

축제 - a festival

게임을 하다 - to play games

쉬다 - to rest/relax

시내에 가다 - go downtown

얘기하다 - to talk/chat (with)

주로 - mainly; mostly

보통 - usually; normally

제일 좋아하는 명절을 왜 좋아해요? [Why do you like your favorite holiday?]

맛있다 - to be delicious

재미있다 - fun; interesting

일하지 않다 - to not work

휴일 - a rest day; a day off

다니다 - to attend

그냥 - just; only; simply

만나다 - to meet

선물을 받다 - to get/receive a present/gift

의상을 입다 - to wear a cos-tume

육하원칙

제일 좋아하는 명절은 뭐예요?
[je-il jo-a-ha-neun myeong-jeo-reun mwo-e-yo?]

Developing Your Answer

제일 좋아하는 명절은 뭐예요?	What's your favorite holiday?
제가 제일 좋아하는 명절은 설날이에요.	[My favorite holiday is Seollal (Korean New Year).]
저는 크리스마스를 제일 좋아해요.	[I like Christmas the most.]
힌두교의 축제 홀리를 정말 좋아해요.	[I really like the Hindu festival Holi.]
제 생각에는 할로윈이 제일 좋아요.	[In my opinion Halloween is the best.]
제가 제일 좋아하는 명절은 콴자예요.	[My favorite holiday is Kwanzaa.]

Your Turn:

누구하고 같이 명절을 축하해요?	Who do you celebrate the holidays with?
매년 친척들하고 같이 하누카를 보내요.	[I spend Hanukkah with my relatives every year.]
친구들하고 같이 새해를 축하해요.	[I celebrate New Year's Day with my friends.]
가족하고 같이 먹고 놀아요.	[I eat with my family and have fun.]
애인하고 같이 발렌타인 데이를 보내요.	[I spend Valentine's Day with my partner.]
부활절에는 항상 부모님하고 보내요.	[I always celebrate Easter with my parents.]

Your Turn:

육하원칙

제일 좋아하는 명절은 뭐예요?
[je-il jo-a-ha-neun myeong-jeo-reun mwo-e-yo?]

Developing Your Answer

명절을 어떻게 보내요?	How do you spend the holidays?
부모님의 집에서 다 같이 시간을 보내요.	[We spend time all together at my parents' house.]
제 친구들이랑 축제를 다녀요.	[I attend a festival with my friends.]
하루 종일 친척들하고 같이 요리해요.	[I cook together with my relatives all day.]
보통 집에서 쉬면서 게임을 해요.	[I usually rest at home and play games.]
주로 친구랑 시내에 가요.	[I go downtown with my friends.]

Your Turn:

제일 좋아하는 명설을 왜 좋아해요?	Why do you like your favorite holiday?
가족을 볼 수 있어서 추석이 제일 좋아요.	[Chuseok is the best, since I can see my family.]
맛있는 음식을 먹을 수 있기 때문이에요.	[Because I get to eat delicious food.]
선물을 받기 때문에 크리스마스가 좋아요.	[I like Christmas, because I get presents.]
일하지 않아서 설날을 제일 좋아해요.	[I like Seollal the most because I don't work.]
그냥 재미있어서 좋아해요.	[I just like it because it's fun.]

Your Turn:

쓰기

제일 좋아하는 명절은 뭐예요?
[je-il jo-a-ha-neun myeong-jeo-reun mwo-e-yo?]

Try Writing Your Own Answer

1) Write your own answer below to the question -- 제일 좋아하는 명절은 뭐예요? --

2) Get your answer corrected and rewrite your corrected answer here:

You can post your writing on an app/website like *Hellotalk* or *Hinative* for free corrections.

대화

제일 좋아하는 명절은 뭐예요?
[je-il jo-a-ha-neun myeong-jeo-reun mwo-e-yo?]

Example Conversation

시우: 소피씨, 제일 좋아하는 명절은 뭐예요?
What's your favorite holiday, Sophie?

소피: 저는 크리스마스가 좋아요. 시우씨는요?
I like Christmas. How about you, Shi-woo?

시우: 저는 설날을 좋아해요. 새뱃돈을 받잖아요. 돈 싫어하는 사람이 있나요? 하하
I like Seollal. Since you get pocket money. Is there anyone who doesn't like money? Haha.

소피: 미국에서는 보통 명절에 돈을 받지 않아서 아쉬워요. 저도 돈을 받**고 싶어요**. 하하
In America we usually don't get money on holidays - it's a shame. I want to get money, too. Haha.

시우: 아 그렇구나. 하하 그럼 크리스마스를 좋아하는 이유가 뭐예요?
Oh, really? Haha. Well, what's the reason you like Christmas, then?

소피: 흠... 선물을 받는 거예요! 아, 이유가 좀 비슷하네요. 하하
Hm... getting presents! Oh, our reasons are kind of similar, huh. Haha.

시우: ㄱㅊ 선물 싫어하는 사람이 없죠. 하하
Yeah they are. Nobody hates gifts right? Haha.

문화

Culture Note

설날

설날 (Seollal), or Korean New Year, takes place on the first day of the Lunar Calendar, and is one of the most celebrated holidays in Korea. Seollal is a family holiday, so on Seollal people often travel back to their hometowns (specifically to their parents'/grandparents' houses) from all over the country so that the whole family can spend time together.

One main tradition observed on Seollal is the traditional New Year's bow (세배). When performing 세배, children wear traditional Korean clothing called hanbok (한복), bow before their elders, and after doing so, receive pocket money known as saebaet-ton (세뱃돈).

Another big part of this holiday is the food. One food commonly eaten on Seollal is tteokguk (떡국), or rice-cake soup. Traditionally, the act of eating tteokguk on Seollal makes you one year older. Although people do still celebrate their individual birthdays in Korea, Seollal is the day where everyone in Korea collectively ages by one year. A benefit of this system is that it allows all children to speak casual language (반말) with each other, because they are all the exact same Korean age.

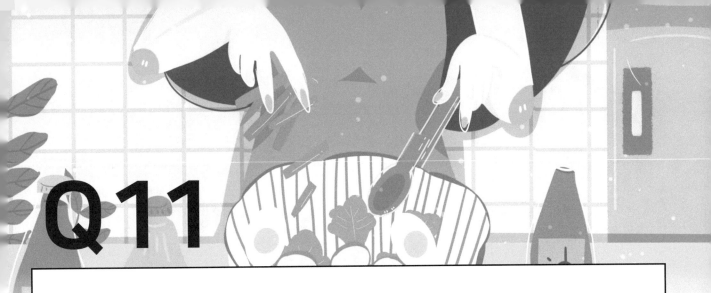

Q11

요리하는 것을 좋아하세요?

[yo-ri-ha-neun geo-seul jo-a-ha-se-yo?]

Do you like to cook?

요리하다 : to cook	
V~는 것 : verb nominalization; used to change a verb into it's noun form	
~을/를 : object particle	
좋아하다 : to like	
~(으)세요 : honorific present tense sentence ending	

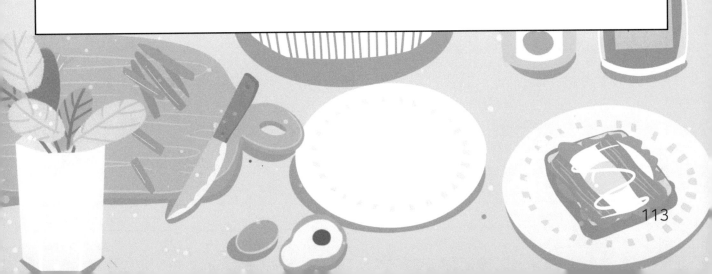

대답

요리하는 것을 좋아하세요?
[yo-ri-ha-neun geo-seul jo-a-ha-se-yo?]
Do you like to cook?

저는 요리하는 것을 별로 좋아하지 않아요.
부엌이 작고 어두워서 요리할 때 답답하거든요.
외식하는 것이 훨씬 더 편해요.

I don't really like cooking.
My kitchen is small and dark, so when I cook it's uncomfortable.
Going out to eat is much more convenient.

Answer Breakdown

Vocabulary	Grammar
Nouns	~은/는 Topic Particle
저 - I; me	~을/를 Object Particle
별로 - not really; rarely	~이/가 Subject Particle
부엌 - kitchen	V~는 것
훨씬 더 - much more; way more	A/V~지 않다
Action Verbs	Present Tense ~아/어요
요리하다 - to cook	Words of Frequency
좋아하다 - to like	A/V~고
외식하다 - to dine out; to go out to eat	A/V~아/어서
Descriptive Verbs	더 & 덜
작다 - to be small	A/V~(으)ㄹ 때, N 때
어둡다 - to be dark	A/V~거든(요)
답답하다 - to be to be frustrating/suffocating/ stuffy/uncomfortable	
편하다 - convenient; comfortable	

The grammar is color-coded to match chapters in *Conversational Korean Grammar.*

설명

Grammar Spotlight

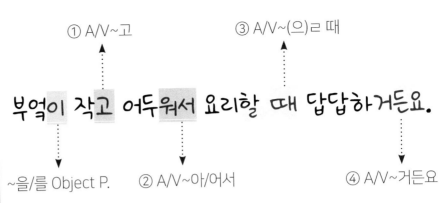

① A/V~고

③ A/V~(으)ㄹ 때

부엌이 작고 어두워서 요리할 때 답답하거든요.

~을/를 Object P.

② A/V~아/어서

④ A/V~거든요

① A/V~고: This form attaches to a verb stem to connect two clauses in a sentence together with the meaning "and". In the sentence above it connects the verb "작다" (to be small) and the verb "어둡다" (to be dark), making "작**고** 어두워요" (it's small and dark).
NOTE: 어둡다 is a ㅂ irregular verb.

식사를 하**고** 와인을 한 잔 마셔요.	I have a meal and drink a glass of wine.
야채를 먼저 썰**고** 고기를 썰어요.	First I chop the vegetables, and then the meat.

② A/V~아/어서: This form connects two clauses, and is used when clause 1 of a sentence is the reason that clause 2 happens. It means "because/so/since." In the sentence above it attaches to "어둡다" (to be dark), making "어두**워서**" (it's dark, so.... / since it's dark...).

부엌이 넓고 밝**아서** 요리하기 편해요.	My kitchen is big and bright, so it's great for cooking.
제 식사는 신선하고 야채가 많**아서** 건강해요.	My meals are fresh with lots of veggies, so they're healthy.

③ A/V~(으)ㄹ 때: This form connects two clauses, and means "when" something happens. In the example above it combines with "요리하다" (to cook), making "요리**할 때**..." (when I cook...)

양파를 **썰 때** 눈물이 나서 힘들어요.	I cry when I cut onions, so it's tough.
자취**할 때** 부엌이 없어서 외식을 자주 했어요.	I had no kitchen when I moved out, so I ate out a lot.

④ A/V~거든요: When attached to the verb stem, **~거든요** means "because/since". In the example above, the verb "답답하다" (to be uncomfortable) becomes 답답하**거든요** (because it's uncomfortable). This gives a reason for the preceding sentence "I don't really like cooking."

어제 외식할 때 기분이 안 좋았어요.	When I went out to eat yesterday, I wasn't happy.
왜냐하면 그 식당 밥이 너무 별로였**거든요**.	Since the food at the restaurant was not very good.
배고플 때 샌드위치를 자주 먹어요.	When I'm hungry I often have a sandwich.
왜냐하면 만들기 쉽고 맛있**거든요**.	Because they're easy to make and taste good.

문법

A/V~(으)ㄹ 때
[To talk about the times that you do things]

Grammar Practice

A/V~(으)ㄹ 때

This form is used to talk about "when" something happens. Attach **~ㄹ 때** to verb stems ending in a vowel, and **~을 때** to verb stems ending in a consonant.

Scan the QR code to view a short grammar lesson PDF.

Given the English sentence below, use the grammar form above to write the equivalent expression in Korean. Using "저는" is optional.

1. When I study Korean, I listen to music.　　공부하다 - study | 음악 - listen | *듣다 - listen

....

2. When I'm driving, I don't use my phone.　　운전하다 - drive | 핸드폰 - phone | *쓰다 - use

....

3. When I go home, I take the bus.　　집 - home | 가다 - go | 버스 - bus | 타다 - take

....

4. When I eat dinner, I watch TV.　　저녁 - dinner | 먹다 - eat | 텔레비전 - TV

....

5. When I was young, I liked school.　　어리다 - young | 학교 - school | 좋아하다 - like

....

*Irregular Verb: Be aware that this verb conjugates irregularly.

Please be aware that not all sentences have one exact translation, so answers may vary slightly.

 **어휘**

요리하는 것을 좋아하세요?
[yo-ri-ha-neun geo-seul jo-a-ha-se-yo?]

Recommended Vocabulary

요리하는 것을 좋아하세요? [Do you like to cook?]

좋다 - to be good; likeable

좋아하다 - to like

싫다 - to be bad; unlikeable

싫어하다 - to dislike; to hate

쉽다 - to be easy/simple

어렵다 - to be difficult/hard

힘들다 - difficult; hard; tiring

재미있다 - fun; interesting

바쁘다 - to be busy

맛있다 - to be delicious

맛없다 - to taste bad

귀찮다 - to be a hassle/pain

배달시켜 먹다 - eat take out

요리하다 - to cook

외식하다 - to go out to eat

요리할 때 주로 무슨 음식을 만들어요? [What do you usually make when you cook?]

한국 음식 - Korean food

서양 음식 - western food

보통 - usually; normally

만들다 - to make

식사하다 - to have a meal

주로 - mainly; mostly

밥 - 1) a meal 2) white rice

식사 - a meal

수프 - soup

파스타 - pasta

샌드위치 - a sandwich

샐러드 - salad

(야채)볶음 - (veggie) stir-fry

배달 음식 - delivery food

간단한 음식 - simple foods

언제 요리를 해요? [When do you cook?]

배고프다 - to be hungry

주말 - weekend

시간이 있다 - to have time

매일 - every day

저녁 - evening; dinner

평일 - weekdays

아침 - morning; breakfast

미리 재료를 준비하다 - to meal prep

특별한 날 - a special day

새로운 것 - something new

땡기다 - to crave

요리를 잘 해요? [Can you cook well]

레시피 - a recipe

따라하다 - to follow

서투르다 - clumsy; unskilled

잘 하다 - to do well

잘 되다 - to turn out well

잘 못 하다 - to not do well

경험이 없다 - inexperienced

경험이 많다 - experienced

연습하다 - to practice

117

요리하는 것을 좋아하세요?
[yo-ri-ha-neun geo-seul jo-a-ha-se-yo?]

Developing Your Answer

요리하는 것을 좋아하세요?	Do you like to cook?
네, 요리하는 걸 아주 좋아해요!	[Yes, I really like to cook!]
아니요, 저는 요리하는 게 싫어요.	[No, I hate cooking.]
네, 근데 요즘 바빠서 주로 배달시켜 먹어요.	[Yes, but lately I'm busy, so I mainly eat take out.]
아니요, 귀찮아서 좋아하지 않아요.	[No, cooking is a hassle, so I don't like it.]
요리는 어렵지만 좋아하는 편이에요.	[Cooking is difficult, but I like it.]

Your Turn:

요리할 때 주로 무슨 음식을 만들어요?	What do you usually make when you cook?
요리할 때 주로 한국 음식을 만들어요.	[When I cook I mainly make Korean food.]
보통 서양 음식을 만들어요.	[I usually make western food.]
요리할 때 파스타나 수프를 만들어요.	[When I cook I make pasta or soup.]
저는 불고기를 잘 만들 수 있어요.	[I'm good at making bulgogi.]
요리를 하는 것보다 외식을 자주 해요.	[I eat out more often than I cook.]

Your Turn:

118

요리하는 것을 좋아하세요?
[yo-ri-ha-neun geo-seul jo-a-ha-se-yo?]

Developing Your Answer

언제 요리를 해요?	When do you cook?
특별한 것이 땡길 때 요리해요.	[I cook food when I'm craving something special.]
시간 있을 때 미리 재료를 준비해요.	[When I have time I meal prep.]
매일 저녁 맛있는 음식을 만들어요.	[Every evening I make a delicious meal.]
주말엔 요리하지만 평일엔 안 해요.	[I cook on the weekends, but not on the weekdays.]
특별한 날에만 요리해요.	[I only cook on special occasions.]

Your Turn:

요리를 잘 해요?	Can you cook well?
저는 요리를 잘 못 하지만 좋아해요.	[I can't really cook, but I like to.]
저는 잘 못 하지만 남편은 잘 해요.	[I can't, but my husband is good at it.]
저는 잘 하는 편인 것 같아요.	[I think I'm pretty good at cooking.]
레시피를 따라하면 잘 되는 편이에요.	[If I have a recipe it turns out okay.]
저는 요리에 서투른 편이에요.	[I'm pretty lousy when it comes to cooking.]

Your Turn:

쓰기

요리하는 것을 좋아하세요?
[yo-ri-ha-neun geo-seul jo-a-ha-se-yo?]

Try Writing Your Own Answer

1) Write your own answer below to the question   -- 요리하는 것을 좋아하세요? --

2) Get your answer corrected and rewrite your corrected answer here:

You can post your writing on an app/website like *Hellotalk* or *Hinative* for free corrections.

대화

요리하는 것을 좋아하세요?
[yo-ri-ha-neun geo-seul jo-a-ha-se-yo?]

Example Conversation

은우: 톰씨, 요리하는 걸 좋아해요?
Tom, do you like cooking?

톰: 네, 좋아해요! 저는 자주 요리하는 편이에요. 은우씨는요?
Yes I like it! I cook pretty often. How about you, Eun-woo?

은우: 저는 좋아하지만 시간이 좀 없어서 배달음식을 자주 먹어요.
I like it, but I don't really have time so I often eat delivery food.

톰: 아, 저도 너무 바쁠 **땐** 배달음식을 많이 먹어요. 보통 어떤 음식을 주문하세요?
Ah, when I'm busy I eat a lot of delivery food too. What do you usually order?

은우: 주로 피자나 치킨을 먹어요. 근데, 톰씨가 요리**할 때** 보통 어떤 음식을 만들어요?
I mostly eat pizza or fried chicken. But Tom, what do you usually make when you cook?

톰: 저는 양식이 땡**길 때** 파스타나 스테이크를 자주 요리해요. 아니면 된장찌개나 삼겹살을 먹어요.
When I'm craving western food, I often cook pasta or steak. If not, I have doen-jang-jjigae or grilled pork belly.

은우: 와, 한식이랑 양식을 모두 요리할 수 있군요! 대단해요.
Wow, so you can cook both Korean and western food! That's amazing.

문화

요리하는 것을 좋아하세요?
[yo-ri-ha-neun geo-seul jo-a-ha-se-yo?]

Culture Note

삼겹살

Korean food is diverse and has a lot to offer. Samgyeopsal (삼겹살) is a dish that is especially popular with both locals and foreigners alike. Samgyeopsal literally means "three layer meat," and refers to strips of thick pork belly.

When eating samgyeopsal, diners cook the meat themselves at their table on either a gas or charcoal grill. As the meat cooks, diners turn the meat using tongs and cut the strips into bite-size chunks using scissors. These chunks are grilled until golden and crispy on the edges, and eaten fresh from the grill with accompanying side dishes (반찬).

While eating samgyeopsal, it is popular to make lettuce wraps called "ssam" (쌈). To make 쌈, place your grilled pork and desired 반찬 (e.g. rice, freshly pickled onions, sliced green onions, kimchi, pickled radish, etc.) on a leaf of lettuce, and then gather the lettuce up into a wrap and eat it in one big bite.
Note: Some people consider it bad luck to eat 쌈 in more than one bite - so try not to pack it too full!

최근에 어떤 고민이 있어요?

[chwe-geu-ne eo-tteon go-mi-ni i-sseo-yo?]

What are you worried about lately?

최근 : recently	
~에 : prepositional time particle	
어떤 : what; what (kind of); which	
고민 : a concern; a worry	
~이/가 : subject particle	
있다 : to exist; to have	
~아요/어요: informal polite present tense	

대답

최근에 어떤 고민이 있어요?

[chwe-geu-ne eo-tteon go-mi-ni i-sseo-yo?]

What are you worried about lately?

요즘 수능이 많이 걱정돼요.
시험에 떨어지고 원하는 대학에 못 갈까 봐 걱정돼요.
근데 아빠에게 전화해서 얘기하면 스트레스가 좀 풀려요.

I'm worried about my college entrance exam lately.
I'm scared I might fail the exam and not be able to go to the college I want.
But when I call my dad and talk with him, it relieves the stress a bit.

Answer Breakdown

Vocabulary	Grammar
Nouns	~이/가 Subject Particle
요즘 – nowadays, these days, lately	Present Tense ~아/어요
수능 – college entrance exam	N~에 V
시험 – test; exam	Place~에 가다/오다
대학 – college; university	못 V
근데 – But/However	A/V~고, N~(이)고
아빠 – (my) dad	A/V~아/어서, N~(이)라서
좀 – a little bit	A/V~(으)면
Action Verbs	V~는 N
떨어지다 – to fail; (lit. to fall/drop)	N~께/에게/한테
원하다 – to want/desire	A~게/이/히
가다 – to go	A/V~(으)ㄹ까 봐
전화하다 – to call someone (on the phone)	
얘기하다 – to talk/chat(with); to converse	
Descriptive Verbs	
많다 – to be many	
걱정되다 – to be worried (about)	
스트레스가 풀리다 – to relieve one's stress	

124   The grammar is color-coded to match chapters in *Conversational Korean Grammar*.

설명

Grammar Spotlight

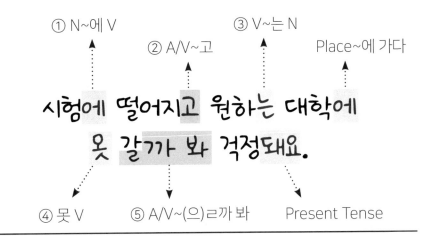

① N~에 V
② A/V~고
③ V~는 N
Place~에 가다

시험에 떨어지고 원하는 대학에
못 갈까 봐 걱정돼요.

④ 못 V
⑤ A/V~(으)ㄹ까 봐
Present Tense

---

① N~에 V: the particle **~에** is used with many nouns in the place of English prepositions like "in/at/on/to", etc. The phrase "시험**에** 떨어지다" means "to fail in/at/on one's exam."

면접**에** 떨어질 것 같아요.	I think I'm going to fail my interview.
엄마가 병원**에** 입원할 것 같아요.	I think my mom will be admitted to the hospital.

② A/V~고 : **~고** is used to connect two clauses in a sentence together with the meaning "and". "시험에 떨어지다" (to fail an exam) becomes "시험에 떨어지**고**..." (I fail my exam and...).

면접에 떨어지**고** 많이 속상했어요.	I failed my interview, and I was really disappointed.
대학에 합격하**고** 등록금이 걱정됐어요.	I got into college, and I'm worried about the tuition.

③ V~는 N: the verb "원하다" (to want/desire) is an action verb. To change action verbs into their adjective forms, we need to attach **~는** to the verb stem (원하**는** - desired/wanted) . So "원하**는** 대학" is one's "desired college."

원하**는** 대학에는 못 가고 취업했어요.	I didn't get into my desired college, and then I got a job.
키우**는** 고양이가 늙고 병들었어요.	My cat is old and sick.

④ 못 V: you can place **못** before a verb to say that you cannot do that verb. In the example above, **못** is placed before the verb "가다" (to go), becoming "**못** 가요" (I can't go).

지금 사는 집이 너무 좁아서 더 이상 **못** 살아요.	My house is too small, so I can't live here any longer.
처음 보는 사람하고는 얘기를 잘 **못** 해요.	I'm not good at talking to someone I've just met.

⑤ A/V~(으)ㄹ까 봐 : Attach **~(으)ㄹ 까 봐** to talk about something you are worried or concerned about. It is usually followed by a verb like "두렵다" (afraid of) or "걱정되다" (worried about).

서울대학교에 못 **갈까 봐** 걱정돼요.	I'm worried that I can't go to Seoul University.
수술이 잘 못 **될까 봐** 걱정돼요.	I'm worried the surgery won't go well.

문법

A/V~고, N(이)고
[To connect clauses with "and"]

Grammar Practice

A/V~고, N(이)고
This form is used to connect two clauses with the meaning of "and." Attach **~고** to the final verb in the first clause. Attach overall tense to the final verb in the second clause.

Scan the QR code to view a short grammar lesson PDF.

Given the English sentence below, use the grammar form above to write the equivalent expression in Korean. Including "저는" in your sentences is optional.

1. I failed my exam and I was sad.

시험에 떨어지다 - to fail a test | *슬프다 - sad

....

2. I ate a meal and did my homework.

밥을 먹다 - eat a meal | 숙제하다 - do homework

....

3. The strawberries are big and sweet.

딸기 - strawberry | 크다 - big | 달다 - sweet

....

4. We watched a movie and ate a meal.

영화 - movie | 보다 - to watch | 밥 - a meal

....

5. Today I'll meet a friend and study.

친구 - friend | 만나다 - meet | 공부하다 - study

....

*Irregular Verb: Be aware that this verb conjugates irregularly.

Please be aware that not all sentences have one exact translation, so answers may vary slightly.

어휘

최근에 어떤 고민이 있어요?
[chwe-geu-ne eo-tteon go-mi-ni i-sseo-yo?]

Recommended Vocabulary

최근에 어떤 고민이 있어요? [What are you worried about lately?]

기말고사 - final exam

중간고사 - midterm exam

입원하다 - to be hospitalized

미래 - the future

면접 - a job interview

실수하다 - make a mistake

시험에 떨어지다 - fail a test

죽음 - death

운전하다 - to drive

건강 - health

지구온난화 - global warming

발표 - a presentation

고민하는 이유가 뭐예요? [Why are you worried about it?]

무섭다 - to be scary

걱정되다 - to be worried (about)

고민이 있다 - to have concerns/worries

두렵다 - to be afraid (of)

망치다 - to ruin; to mess up

아프다 - to be hurt/sick

나빠지다 - to worsen

외롭다 - to be lonely

위험하다 - to be dangerous

사고가 나다 - to have an accident

문제 - a problem/issue

실패하다 - to fail

언제 이런 고민을 느껴요? [When do you worry about it?]

아픈 환자 - a sick patient

차 사고가 나다 - to have a car accident

수업에 따라잡다 - to keep up in a class

심하게 - seriously; gravely

혼자 있다 - to be alone

자취를 하다 - to move out

듣다 - to listen; to hear

뉴스 - the news

비가 오다 - to rain

고민을 덜기 위해 무엇을 해요? [What do you do to ease your worries?]

낮잠을 자다 - to take a nap

운동을 하다 - to exercise

텔레비전을 보다 - watch TV

독서하다 - to read (hobby)

음악을 틀다 - put on music

목욕을 하다 - to take a bath

전화하다 - to make a phone call; to call

스트레스가 풀리다 - to relieve stress

스트레스를 받다 - to get stressed; to be stressed

육하원칙

최근에 어떤 고민이 있어요?
[chwe-geu-ne eo-tteon go-mi-ni i-sseo-yo?]

Developing Your Answer

최근에 어떤 고민이 있어요?	What are you worried about lately?
저는 다음 달에 기말고사가 있어요.	[I have my final exam next month.]
엄마가 병원에 입원해 계세요.	[My mother is in the hospital.]
시험에 떨어질까 봐 두려워요.	[I'm afraid that I'll fail my exam.]
지구온난화가 걱정돼요.	[I'm worried about global warming.]
내일 있을 면접이 걱정돼요.	[I'm nervous about my job interview tomorrow.]

Your Turn:

고민하는 이유가 뭐예요?	Why are you worried about it?
발표를 망칠까 봐 두려워요.	[I'm afraid that I'll fail my presentation.]
엄마 상태가 더 나빠질까 봐 두려워요.	[I'm afraid my mom's condition will get worse.]
실패하면 대학에 못 갈까 봐 두려워요.	[I'm afraid I can't go to college if I fail.]
죽을 때 아플까 봐 두려워요.	[I'm afraid that dying will be painful.]
계속 취업에 실패할까 봐 두려워요.	[I'm afraid I'll keep failing to get a job.]

Your Turn:

육하원칙

최근에 어떤 고민이 있어요?
[chwe-geu-ne eo-tteon go-mi-ni i-sseo-yo?]

Developing Your Answer

언제 이런 고민을 느껴요?	When do you worry about it?
아픈 환자들을 보고 죽음이 두려워졌어요.	[I'm worried about death when I see sick people.]
자취를 시작하고 혼자 있는게 무서워졌어요.	[I moved out, and being alone became scary.]
뉴스를 들을 때 지구온난화가 걱정됐어요.	[I worry about global warming when I hear the news.]
학기 초에 수업을 따라잡지 못 할까 봐 걱정돼요.	[At the start of the semester I worry I can't keep up.]
비가 오면 차 사고가 날까 봐 두려워요.	[I'm afraid of being in a car accident when it rains.]

Your Turn:

고민을 덜기 위해 무엇을 해요?	What do you do to ease your worries?
스트레스를 받을 때 낮잠을 자요.	[When I'm stressed I take a nap.]
엄마가 걱정될 때 전화해요.	[When I'm worried about my mom, I call her.]
운동을 하면 스트레스가 풀리는 것 같아요.	[I think exercising relieves stress.]
독서를 하면 걱정거리가 사라져요.	[When I'm reading, all my worries disappear.]
혼자 있고 너무 조용할 때 음악을 틀어요.	[When I'm alone and it's too quiet, I put music on.]

Your Turn:

쓰기

최근에 어떤 고민이 있어요?
[chwe-geu-ne eo-tteon go-mi-ni i-sseo-yo?]

Try Writing Your Own Answer

1) Write your own answer below to the question   -- 최근에 어떤 고민이 있어요? --

2) Get your answer corrected and rewrite your corrected answer here:

You can post your writing on an app/website like *Hellotalk* or *Hinative* for free corrections.

대화

최근에 어떤 고민이 있어요?
[chwe-geu-ne eo-tteon go-mi-ni i-sseo-yo?]

Example Conversation

수호: 도윤씨, 최근에 어떤 고민이 있어요?
What are you worried about these days, Doyoon?

도윤: 지금 수능 공부를 하고 있어요. 근데 수능에 떨어질까 봐 걱정돼요.
I'm studying for the college entrance exam at the moment. But I'm worried I'll fail.

수호: 네... 저는 더 좋은 점수를 받으려고 수능을 두 번 치렀어요.
Yeah... I took the test twice so that I could get a good score.

도윤: 아, 그래요. 그래서 더 좋은 점수를 받았어요?
Oh, I see. And did you get a better score?

수호: 그런 것 같아요. 완벽하지는 않았지만 만족할 만한 점수였어요. 도윤씨는 수능 때문에 스트레스를 많이 받아요?
I think so. It wasn't perfect, but it was a score I could be satisfied with. Is it really stressing you out?

도윤: 네... 요즘 스트레스를 많이 받아요. 수호씨도 스트레스를 많이 받았어요? 어떻게 해야 돼요?
Yes... I've been really stressed out lately. Were you stressed too? What should I do?

수호: 너무 심하게 자책하지 밀고 페이스를 유지아면서 잠을 숭분히 사세요. 시금은 힘들지만 지나고나면 다 괜찮을 거예요. 힘내세요.
Don't be too hard on yourself, pace yourself, and get enough sleep. It's difficult right now, but once you get past it, it'll all be okay. Hang in there.

문화

최근에 어떤 고민이 있어요?
[chwe-geu-ne eo-tteon go-mi-ni i-sseo-yo?]

Culture Note

수능 The College Scholastic Ability Test ("대학수학능력시험" or "수능" for short) is a standardized test that students must take to graduate from high school. It is also very important for college entrance.

Korean students spend most of their childhoods studying and preparing for this test, often attending after-school academies or working with private tutors in order to achieve their desired grade. Some people even take the test multiple times. Their grade on the test can affect whether they go to college, their future job prospects, income, where they will live, and even their future relationships.

The exam is eight hours long and is held every November. On test day, the stock market opens late, buses and metro services are increased, planes are grounded, and crowds gather outside testing sites to cheer on the students. [4]

Q 13

어떤 종류의 음악을 좋아하세요?

[eo-tteon jong-nyu-e eu-ma-geul jo-a-ha-se-yo?]

What kind of music do you like?

어떤 : what; what kind of; which
종류 : kind/type/sort/variety
N ~의 : possessive particle
음악 : music
~을/를 : object particle
좋아하다 : to like
~(으)세요 : honorific present tense sentence ending

대답

어떤 종류의 음악을 좋아하세요?

[eo-tteon jong-nyu-e eu-ma-geul jo-a-ha-se-yo?]

What kind of music do you like?

저는 힙합을 좋아해요.
제가 제일 좋아하는 힙합 밴드의 콘서트를 보러
한국에 가고 싶은데 아직 안 가 봤어요.

I like hip-hop music.
I want to go to Korea to see my favorite hip-hop band's concert,
but I haven't been there yet.

Answer Breakdown

Vocabulary	Grammar
Nouns	~은/는 Topic Particle
저 - I/me	~을/를 Object Particle
힙합 - hip-hop	~이/가 Subject Particle
제 - my	Present Tense ~아/어요
제일 - most; best	Place~에 가다/오다
밴드 - band(s)	안 A/V
콘서트 - a concert	A/V~았/었다 Past Tense
한국 - Korea	V~고 싶다
아직 - still; yet	가장 & 제일
Action Verbs	V~는 N
좋아하다 - to like	V~아/어 보다
보다 - to see/watch	N의
가다 - to go	A/V~(으)ㄴ/는데
	V~(으)러 가다/오다

The grammar is color-coded to match chapters in *Conversational Korean Grammar*.

설명

Grammar Spotlight

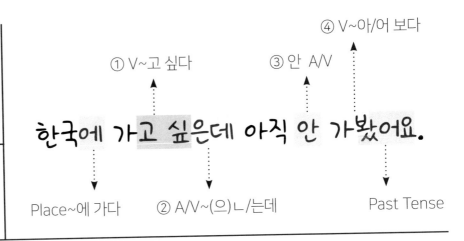

④ V~아/어 보다

① V~고 싶다

③ 안 A/V

한국에 가고 싶은데 아직 안 가봤어요.

Place~에 가다

② A/V~(으)ㄴ/는데

Past Tense

① **V~고 싶다:** Attach **~고 싶다** to a verb stem to say that you "want to do" that verb. In the example above, it attaches to the verb "가다"(to go), becoming "가**고 싶어요.**" (I want to go).

좋아하는 가수의 음악을 잘 부르**고 싶어요.**   I want to sing my favorite singer's music well.

운전할 때 조용한 음악을 듣**고 싶어요.**   I want to listen to quiet music when I drive.

② **A/V~(으)ㄴ/는데:** This form attaches to a verb stem, and is used when you are giving some background information. It connects two clauses in a sentence together with the meaning "and", "but", or "so". In the sentence above we have "가고 싶**은데**..." (I want to go, but...).

노래를 잘 부르고 싶**은데** 음치예요.   I want sing well, but I'm tone-deaf.

콘서트에 가고 싶**은데** 티켓이 너무 비싸요 .   I want to go to the concert, but the tickets are too expensive.

③ **안 A/V: 안** is placed before the verb, and is used to make a negative sentence. With separable 하다 verbs you must put **안** between the noun and 하다. It means "don't/not/isn't." In the example above it comes before "가다," making "**안** 가 봤어요." (I haven't been/tried going).

음악감상은 좋아하는데 노래는 잘 **안** 불러요.   I like listening to music, but I don't really sing.

그 노래는 가사는 좋은데 멜로디는 **안** 좋아요.   That song's lyrics are good, but the melody isn't.

④ **V~아/어 보다:** This form is used to talk about trying to do something, or "giving something a try" (often for the first time). In the past tense, the form **~아/어 봤다** can be used to say "I tried". In the example above "가다" (to go) becomes "**가 봤어요**" (I went/tried going).

NOTE: Although this form is used for experiences you are "giving a try," the word "try" is not always natural in English (e.g. "try going" sounds a bit unnatural in English).

새 앨범은 아직 안 들**어 봤어요.**   I haven't listened to the new album yet.

오페라를 좋아하는데 아직 안 **가 봤어요.**   I like the opera, but I haven't been yet.

135

문법

A/V~(으)ㄴ/는데
[To connect clauses with "and/but/so/..."]

Grammar Practice

A/V~(으)ㄴ/는데

Attach ~ㄴ데 to adjectives ending with a vowel, and ~은데 to adjectives ending with a consonant. Attach ~는데 to the adjectives "있다" and "없다," and to all action verbs.

Scan the QR code to view a short grammar lesson PDF.

Given the English sentence below, use the grammar form above to write the equivalent expression in Korean. Including "저는" in your sentences is optional.

1. The weather is cold, but I want to swim.   날씨 - weather | *춥다 - cold | 수영하다 - swim

....

2. I want to sleep, but I have homework.   자다 - sleep | 숙제 - homework | 있다 - have

....

3. I like music, but I can't sing.   음악 - music | 좋아하다 - to like | 노래하다 - sing

....

4. The food is tasty, but expensive.   음식 - food | 맛있다 - tasty | 비싸다 - expensive

....

5. It's raining now, but I have no umbrella.   비가 오다 - rain | 우산 - umbrella | 없다 - not have

....

*Irregular Verb: Be aware that this verb conjugates irregularly.

ANSWERS: 1. 날씨가 추운데 수영하고 싶어요. 2. 자고 싶은데 숙제가 있어요. 3. 음악을 좋아하는데 노래를 못 해요. 4. 음식이 맛있는데 비싸요. 5. 지금 비가 오는데 우산이 없어요.

Please be aware that not all sentences have one exact translation, so answers may vary slightly.

어휘

어떤 종류의 음악을 좋아하세요?
[eo-tteon jong-nyu-e eu-ma-geul jo-a-ha-se-yo?]

Recommended Vocabulary

어떤 종류의 음악을 좋아해요? [What kind of music do you like?]

락 / 록 - rock music	팝송 / 팝 - pop music	알앤비 - R&B
이디엠 - EDM	힙합 - hip hop	랩 - rap
발라드 - ballads	댄스 - dance	레게 - reggae
컨트리 - country music	재즈 - jazz	인디 - indie
헤비 메탈 - heavy metal	케이팝 - K-pop	로파이 - lo-fi
블루스 - blues	클래식 - classical music	하우스 - house

언제 음악을 들어요? [When do you listen to music?]

공부하다 - to study	운동을 하다 - to exercise	운전하다 - to drive
일을 하다 - to work	자다 - to sleep	청소하다 - to clean
샤워하다 - to shower	쇼핑하다 - to shop	든다 - to listen; to hear
요리하다 - to cook	산책하다 - to go for a walk	숙제하다 - to do homework

콘서트에 가는 것도 좋아해요? [Do you also like going to concerts?]

라이브 음악 - live music	밴드 - a band	콘서트 - a concert
야외 - outdoors/outdoor	굿즈 - merch/merchandise	재미있다 - fun; interesting
시끄럽다 - to be loud/noisy	붐비다 - to be crowded	콘서트장 - a concert venue

왜 이런 종류의 음악을 좋아해요? [Why do you like this kind of music?]

활기차다 - to be active/lively/upbeat	에너지가 넘치다 - to be full of energy	가수 - a singer
특별한 목소리 - unique voice	인기가 많다 - to be popular	가사 - lyrics
춤을 추다 - to dance	조용하다 - to be quiet	느리다 - to be slow

육하원칙

어떤 종류의 음악을 좋아하세요?
[eo-tteon jong-nyu-e eu-ma-geul jo-a-ha-se-yo?]

Developing Your Answer

어떤 종류의 음악을 좋아해요?	What kind of music do you like?
가장 좋아하는 음악 종류는 락이에요.	[My favorite kind of music is rock.]
최근에 힙합을 가장 많이 들어요.	[I listen to hip hop the most lately.]
포크 음악을 제일 좋아해요.	[Folk music is my favorite.]
저는 케이팝하고 제이팝이 좋아요.	[I like k-pop and j-pop.]
재즈나 알앤비 음악을 가장 많이 들어요.	[I listen to jazz or R&B the most.]

Your Turn:

....

....

....

언제 음악을 들어요?	When do you listen to music?
운동을 할 때 빠른 음악을 들어요.	[I listen to upbeat music while I work out.]
공부할 때 항상 로파이 음악을 들어요.	[I always listen to lo-fi music when I study.]
혼자서 일 할 때 클래식 음악을 자주 들어요.	[When I work alone I often listen to classical music.]
자기 전에 발라드를 듣는 편이에요.	[Before I sleep I tend to listen to ballads.]
저는 운전하면서 재즈 음악을 들어요.	[I listen to jazz music while I drive.]

Your Turn:

....

....

....

육하원칙

어떤 종류의 음악을 좋아하세요?
[eo-tteon jong-nyu-e eu-ma-geul jo-a-ha-se-yo?]

Developing Your Answer

콘서트에 가는 것도 좋아해요?	Do you also like going to concerts?
라이브 음악이 좋아서 콘서트에 자주 가요!	[I like live music, so I go to concerts often!]
시끄럽고 너무 붐벼서 별로 안 가요.	[They're loud and crowded, so I don't really go.]
작은 콘서트장에 가는 것을 좋아해요.	[I like going to smaller venues.]
네 주로 굿즈를 사러 콘서트에 가요.	[Yes I mainly go to concerts to buy merchandise.]
날씨가 좋으면 야외 콘서트가 좋아요.	[I like outdoor concerts when the weather is nice.]

Your Turn:

....

....

....

왜 이런 종류의 음악을 좋아해요?	Why do you like this kind of music?
이디엠은 활기차고 에너지가 넘쳐요.	[EDM is upbeat and full of energy.]
이 밴드는 가사가 정말 좋아요.	[This band's lyrics are really great.]
그 가수는 특별한 목소리를 가지고 있어요.	[The singer has a unique voice.]
케이팝은 춤추기 좋아서 인기가 많아요.	[K-pop is good for dancing, so it's popular.]
느리고 조용해서 잠 잘때 듣기 좋아요.	[It's slow and quiet so it's nice to fall asleep to.]

Your Turn:

....

....

....

어떤 종류의 음악을 좋아하세요?

[eo-tteon chwi-mi-reul jo-a-ha-se-yo?]

Try Writing Your Own Answer

1) Write your own answer below to the question   -- 어떤 종류의 음악을 좋아하세요? --

2) Get your answer corrected and rewrite your corrected answer here:

You can post your writing on an app/website like *Hellotalk* or *Hinative* for free corrections.

대화

어떤 종류의 음악을 좋아하세요?
[eo-tteon jong-nyu-e eu-ma-geul jo-a-ha-se-yo?]

Example Conversation

지아: 메리씨, 어떤 종류의 음악을 좋아하세요?
Mary, what kind of music do you like?

메리: 저는 다양한 종류의 음악 중에서, 케이팝을 가장 좋아해요!
Out of all the different kinds of music, I like K-pop the most!

지아: 오, 저도요! 어떤 그룹을 좋아하세요?
Oh, me too! Which groups do you like?

메리: 너무 많아요. 방탄소년단, 갓세븐, 있지, 엔시티, 스트레이 키즈... 다 좋아해요!
There are so many. BTS, Got7, ITZY, NCT, Stray Kids... I like them all!

지아: 오 많네요! 케이팝을 들으면서 가사를 이해할 수 있어요?
Oh, that's a lot! Can you understand the lyrics while you listen to K-pop?

메리: 흠... 바로 노래를 들으면서 이해하는 건 좀 어려**운데** 나중에 그 노래 가사를 찾아서 모르는 단어나 문법을 배우면 이해할 수 있어요!
Hm... it's hard to understand while I'm listening, but if I look up the lyrics to the songs later and learn the words and grammar I don't know, then I can understand it!

지아: 아, 좋은 방법이네요!
Oh, that's a good method!

어떤 종류의 음악을 좋아하세요?
[eo-tteon jong-nyu-e eu-ma-geul jo-a-ha-se-yo?]

Culture Note

한류

In the mid '90's and early 2000's, the popularity of Korean music and film began to grow and spread worldwide. This spread of popularity became known as "the Korean wave" (한류). A key driver of the Korean wave is Korean pop music, also known as "K-pop." K-pop is usually performed by idol groups - bands formed to include multiple members who perform choreographed singing and dancing routines on stage.

One of the most famous Korean idol groups is BTS, short for "Bangtan Sonyeondan" (방탄소년단) meaning "Bulletproof Boy Scouts" (later expanded to include the English meaning "Beyond the Scene"), which is a South Korean idol group that debuted in June 2013. According to the Hyundai Research Institute, BTS was contributing $3.5 billion annually to the nation's economy in 2020. [6]

K-pop is still hugely popular today; a survey conducted in 18 countries in 2021 showed that around 39% of respondents stated that the K-pop genre was "very popular" in their country. [7]

Q14

보통 어떻게 운동을 하나요?

[bo-tong eo-tteo-ke un-don-geul ha-na-yo?]

How do you usually exercise?

보통 : usually ; normally
어떻게 : how
운동 : exercise; a work out; **운동을 하다** : to work out; to exercise
~을/를 : object particle
V~나요? : an ending used to make a question less direct

대답

보통 어떻게 운동을 하나요?

[bo-tong eo-tteo-ke un-don-geul ha-na-yo?]

How do you usually exercise?

저는 요즘 운동을 시작했지만 잘 못 하고 있어요.

원래 운동을 싫어해서 규칙적으로 하기가 어려운 것 같아요.

즐길 수 있는 운동을 찾고 있어요.

I started working out lately, but I'm not that great at it.

I've always disliked exercising, so I think it's hard for me to do it regularly.

I'm looking for an exercise that I can enjoy doing.

Answer Breakdown

Vocabulary	Grammar
Nouns	~은/는 Topic Particle
저 - I; me	~을/를 Object Particle
요즘 - lately; these days; recently	~이/가 Subject Particle
운동 - exercise; working out	A/V~았/었다 Past Tense
원래 - originally/always	Present Tense ~아/어요
규칙적 - regular	A/V~지만, N~(이)지만
Action Verbs	잘 & 잘 못 V
시작하다 - to start	V~고 있다
하다 - to do	A/V~아/어서
싫어하다 - to dislike; to hate	N~(으)로
즐기다 - to enjoy	V~(으)ㄹ 수 있다/없다
찾다 - to find	V~는 N
Descriptive Verbs	V~기
어렵다 - to be difficult/hard	A/V~(으)ㄴ/는/을 것 같다

설명

Grammar Spotlight

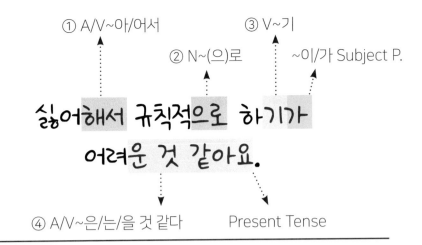

① A/V~아/어서

② N~(으)로

③ V~기

~이/가 Subject P.

싫어해서 규칙적으로 하기가
어려운 것 같아요.

④ A/V~은/는/을 것 같다

Present Tense

① A/V~아/어서: This form connects two clauses, and is used when clause 1 of a sentence is the reason that clause 2 happens. It means "because/so/since." In the example above, it attaches to "싫어하다" (to dislike/hate), making "싫어**해서**..." (I dislike/hate it so...)

아침에 헬스장에 가야 **해서** 못 만나요.	I have to go to the gym in the morning, so we can't meet.
엄마가 등산하러 **가서** 집에 안 계세요.	Mom went hiking, so she's not at home.

② N~(으)로: This form attaches to a noun, allowing you to talk about doing something "with, by, through, or using" that noun. In the example above, **~(으)로** combines with "규칙적" (regular), making 규칙적**으로** (through regularity/regularly).

뛰는 것을 좋아해서 규칙적**으로** 조깅해요.	I like running, so I go jogging regularly.
일이 너무 바빠서 어제 마지막**으로** 헬스장을 갔어요.	Work is too busy, so yesterday I went to the gym for the last time.

③ V~기: V~기 is used to change a verb into it's noun form (it's similar to the ~는 것 form). In the example above the verb "하다" (to do) becomes "하**기**" (doing).

저는 정기적으로 운동하**기**가 어려워요.	For me, exercising regularly is difficult.
매일 줄넘기로 운동하**기**를 좋아해요.	I like to use a jump rope for exercise every day.

④ A/V~(으)ㄴ/는/을 것 같다: This form is used to say "I think (that...)"/"it seems (that...)." There are many forms to choose from depending on the type of verb and the tense, but **~(으)ㄴ 것 같다** is used for descriptive verbs such as "어렵다" (to be difficult). "어렵다" is a ㅂ Irregular Verb, so it becomes "어려**운 것 같아요**" (I think it's difficult) in the example above.

저한테는 스트레칭하기가 더 쉬**운 것 같아요**.	I think stretching is easier for me.
아침에 운동하기가 더 좋**은 것 같아요**.	I think exercising in the morning is better.

145

문법

V~고 있다
[To talk about actions in progress]

Grammar Practice

V~고 있다

Use this form to talk about actions in progress. Either things the subject is currently doing now, or has been doing recently. Attach **~고 있다** to action verb stems.

Scan the QR code to view a short grammar lesson PDF.

Given the English sentence below, use the grammar form above to write the equivalent expression in Korean. Including "저는" in your sentences is optional.

1. I'm eating breakfast now.
지금 - now | 아침 - breakfast | 먹다 - eat

....

2. I'm waiting for a friend at the park.
공원 - park | 친구 - friend | 기다리다 - wait

....

3. These days I'm exercising.
요즘 - these days | 운동하다 - exercise

....

4. These days I'm studying Korean.
한국어 - Korean | 공부하다 - study

....

5. I'm looking into jobs.
직장 - job | 알아보다 - to look into

....

Please be aware that not all sentences have one exact translation, so answers may vary slightly.

어휘

보통 어떻게 운동을 하나요 ?
[bo-tong eo-tteo-ke un-don-geul ha-na-yo?]

Recommended Vocabulary

보통 어떻게 운동을 하나요? [How do you usually exercise?]

운동을 하다 - to exercise	유산소를 하다 - to do cardio	런닝머신 - a treadmill
근육 운동 - muscle building	필라테스 - Pilates	등산 - hiking
달리기 - running	조깅 - jogging	요가 - yoga
스트레칭 - stretching	수영 - swimming	줄넘기 - a jump rope
연도 - weightlifting	산책 - a walk; a stroll	자전거를 타다 - to ride a bike
스포츠 - sports	테니스를 치다 - play tennis	킥복싱을 하다 - to kickbox

주로 언제 운동을 해요? [When do you usually exercise?]

아침 - morning; breakfast	점심 - noon; lunch	저녁 - evening; dinner
밤 - night	시간이 있다 - to have time	평일 - weekdays
오전 - a.m.; the morning	오후 - p.m.; the afternoon	주말 - weekend
출근 전에 - before work	퇴근 후에 - after work	매일 - every day

주로 어디에서 운동을 해요? [Where do you usually exercise?]

헬스장 - a health club/gym	집 - house/home	밖 - outside
동네 - a neighborhood	공원 - a park	등산로 - a hiking trail
운동장 - outdoor sport field	체육관 - a gymnasium	수영장 - a swimming pool

왜 운동을 해요? [Why do you exercise?]

근육을 키우다 - build muscle	건강해지다 - to get healthy	살을 빼다 - to reduce weight
몸매 - one's body/figure	기분이 좋다 - to feel good	정신 건강 - mental health
유연성을 향상시키다 - to improve one's flexibility	스트레스가 풀리다 - to relieve stress	건강을 유지하다 - to stay in shape

147

육하원칙

보통 어떻게 운동을 하나요 ?
[bo-tong eo-tteo-ke un-don-geul ha-na-yo?]

Developing Your Answer

보통 어떻게 운동을 하나요?	How do you normally exercise?
주로 요가도 하고 스트레칭도 해요.	[I usually do both yoga and stretching.]
유산소 할 때 달리기를 해요.	[When I do cardio I go for a run.]
먼저 런닝머신에 달리기를 해요.	[First, I run on the treadmill.]
주로 필라테스나 근육 운동을 해요.	[I usually do Pilates or muscle building exercises.]
등산을 좋아해서 자주 등산해요.	[I like hiking, so I hike often.]

Your Turn:

주로 언제 운동을 해요?	When do you usually exercise?
주말에 보통 요가 수업을 다녀요.	[On the weekend I normally do a yoga class.]
매일 저녁 우리 동네를 산책해요.	[Every evening I walk around my neighborhood.]
아침에 일찍 조깅을 해요.	[I jog early in the morning.]
퇴근 후에 헬스장에 가요.	[I go to the gym after I get off work.]
시간이 있을 때 테니스를 쳐요.	[I play tennis when I have the time.]

Your Turn:

육하원칙

보통 어떻게 운동을 하나요 ?
[bo-tong eo-tteo-ke un-don-geul ha-na-yo?]

Developing Your Answer

주로 어디에서 운동을 해요?	Where do you usually exercise?
매일 아침 집에서 요가를 해요.	[Every morning I do yoga at home.]
가끔 수영 수업을 들어요.	[Sometimes I have swimming classes.]
뒷산 등산로를 자주 이용해요.	[I often use the local hiking trails behind my house.]
저녁에 동네에서 자전거를 타요.	[In the evenings I ride my bike in my neighborhood.]
운동장에서 종종 친구랑 농구를 해요.	[I often play basketball with my friends at the field.]

Your Turn:

왜 운동을 해요?	Why do you excrcise?
더 건강해지고 싶어서 운동을 해요.	[I exercise because I want to get healthier.]
유연성이 나빠서 운동을 하고 있어요.	[I'm exercising because my flexibility is bad.]
조금 더 근육을 키우고 싶어서요.	[Because I want to build up my muscles a bit more.]
건강을 유지하고 싶어서 운동해요.	[I work out because I want to stay healthy.]
운동을 하면 기분이 좋아요.	[When I work out I feel great.]

Your Turn:

쓰기

보통 어떻게 운동을 하나요 ?
[bo-tong eo-tteo-ke un-don-geul ha-na-yo?]

Try Writing Your Own Answer

1) Write your own answer below to the question   -- 보통 어떻게 운동을 하나요? --

2) Get your answer corrected and rewrite your corrected answer here:

대화

보통 어떻게 운동을 하나요 ?
[bo-tong eo-tteo-ke un-don-geul ha-na-yo?]

Example Conversation

메리: 하준씨, 요즘 운동하**고 있어요**?
Are you exercising these days, Hajoon?

하준: 네, 저는 등산을 좋아해요! 그래서 주말엔 자주 산에 가요.
Yes, I like hiking! So I often go to the mountains on the weekend.

메리: 아, 등산! 어디서 주로 해요?
Oh, hiking! Where do you usually hike?

하준: 북한산, 지리산, 설악산, 한라산... 한국에는 좋은 등산로가 아주 많아요.
Bukhansan, Jirisan, Seoraksan, Hallasan... There are lots of good hiking trails in Korea.

메리: 와, 저도 가고 싶어요. 많이 힘들어요?
Wow, I want to go too. Is it very difficult?

하준: 흠... 좀 힘들지만 컨디션이 좋으면 괜찮을 거예요. 그리고 충분한 물을 가지고 좋은 신발을 신으면 돼요.
Hm... it's a bit tough, but if you're in good shape it'll be okay. Just bring enough water and wear good shoes.

메리: 아, 네. 그럼 저도 할 수 있는 것 같아요. 한번 같이 가요!
Oh, okay. Then I think I can do it too. Let's go together sometime!

문화

보통 어떻게 운동을 하나요 ?
[bo-tong eo-tteo-ke un-don-geul ha-na-yo?]

Culture Note

등산

Hiking is South Korea's most popular pastime. Two-thirds of its citizens own a pair of hiking boots and tackle a mountain at least once a year; nearly a third go once a month. In 2018 they spent $2.3bn on hiking gear - more than on cinema tickets or cosmetics. [21]

Mountains cover about 70% of the Korean peninsula [3], creating perfect locations for beautiful hiking trails, even in the middle of busy cities. Whether your hike is long or short, having the right equipment is a must. It is common for people to deck themselves out in high-tech gear, including multiple layers of sweat-wicking and weather-proof clothing, hiking backpacks, and poles. If you go hiking in shorts and flip-flops, you'll probably be fine, but you might get some strange looks.

Food and water are also important. It is common to bring kimbap (rice filled with various fillings like kimchi, egg, carrots, cucumber, etc. wrapped in dried seaweed) and celebrate the end of the hike by drinking Korean rice wine (막걸리).

Q 15

병원에 입원한 적이 있어요?

[byeon-gwo-ne i-bwon-han jeo-gi i-sseo-yo?]

Have you ever been hospitalized?

병원 : a hospital

~에 : location of motion/existence particle

입원하다 : to be hospitalized; to be admitted to a hospital

V~(으)ㄴ 적이 있다/없다 : to have/not have experienced doing some verb

~아요/어요: informal polite present tense

대답

병원에 입원한 적이 있어요?

[byeon-gwo-ne i-bwon-han jeo-gi i-sseo-yo?]

Have you ever been hospitalized?

몇 번 입원해 봤어요.

한번은 땅콩 알레르기 때문에 입원했어요.

3일 정도 입원했는데 아무것도 못 해서 너무 지루했어요.

I've been hospitalized a few times.
One time I was hospitalized for a peanut allergy.
I spent about three days at the hospital, and I couldn't do anything, so it was really boring.

Answer Breakdown

Vocabulary	Grammar
Nouns	~은/는 Topic Particle
몇 번 - a few times	A/V~았/었다 Past Tense
한번 - one time	못 V
땅콩 알레르기 - a peanut allergy	A/V~아/어서
3일 - three days	V~아/어 보다
정도 - about; around	N 때문에
아무것도 - nothing; not anything	N 정도
너무 - really; very; too much	A/V~(으)ㄴ/는데
Action Verbs	
입원하다 - to be hospitalized	
하다 - to do	
Descriptive Verbs	
지루하다 - to be boring	

The grammar is color-coded to match chapters in *Conversational Korean Grammar*.

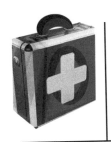

설명

Grammar Spotlight

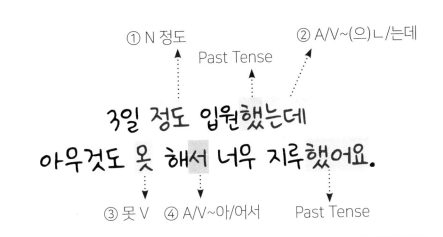

① N 정도   Past Tense   ② A/V~(으)ㄴ/는데

3일 정도 입원했는데
아우것도 옷 해서 너무 지루했어요.

③ 못 V   ④ A/V~아/어서   Past Tense

---

① N 정도: When used after a time noun, **정도** means "about/around/approximately" that amount of time. "3일" means "three days," so "3일 **정도**" means "about/around three days."

3일 **정도** 입원했어요.   I was hospitalized for about three days.
6주 **정도** 깁스를 했어요.   I wore a cast for about six weeks.

② A/V~(으)ㄴ/는데: This form attaches to a verb stem, and is used when you are giving some more background information on the situation. It connects two clauses in a sentence to-gether with the meaning "and", "but", or "so". To use this form in the past tense, attach **~았/었는데**. In the sentence the verb "입원하다" (to be hospitalized) in the past tense becomes "입원**했데**..." (I was hospitalized, and...)

3일 정도 입원했**는데** 병원 밥이 맛있었어요.   I was hospitalized for about three days, and the hospital food was really good.

6개월 정도 물리치료를 했**는데** 효과가 있었어요.   I did physical therapy for about 6 months, and it was effective.

③ 못 V: You can place **못** before a verb when you want to say that you cannot do that verb. In the example above, **못** is placed before the verb "하다" (to do), becoming "**못** 해요" (I can't do).

팔이 부러졌는데 손가락도 **못** 움직였어요.   I broke my arm and I couldn't move my fingers.
아파서 잠도 **못** 잤는데 밥도 **못** 먹었어요.   I was sick, so I couldn't eat and I couldn't sleep.

④ A/V~아/어서: **~아/어서** connects two clauses. It can be attached to a verb stem when you want to say "because/so/since." In the example above, the first clause "아무것도 못 하다" be-comes "아무것도 못 **해서**..." (since/because I couldn't do anything...)

맹장 수술을 해야 **해서** 음식을 못 먹었어요.   I had to have appendix surgery, so I couldn't eat.
6주 정도 못 **걸어서** 짜증났어요.   I couldn't walk for six weeks, so it was annoying.

문법

A/V~아/어서
[To connect clauses with "so/since/because"]

Grammar Practice

A/V~아/어서

Connect two clauses with "so/since/because." Attach **~아/어서** to the final verb of the first clause. There is a secondary meaning of "and (then)" for related sequencial events.

Scan the QR code to view a short grammar lesson PDF.

Given the English sentence below, use the grammar form above to write the equivalent expression in Korean. Including "저는" in your sentences is optional.

1. I'm hungry, so I want to have a meal.

*배고프다 - hungry | 밥 - a meal | 먹다 - eat

....

2. I'm busy, so I don't have time today.

*바쁘다 - busy | 시간 - time | 없다 - don't have

....

3. I didn't study, so I failed the test.

공부하다 - study | 시험 - test | 떨어지다 - fail

....

4. I went to a cafe and drank coffee.

카페 - cafe | 커피 - coffee | 마시다 - drink

....

5. I went to the theater and saw a movie.

영화관 - theater | 영화 - movie | 보다 see

....

*Irregular Verb: Be aware that this verb conjugates irregularly.

ANSWERS: 1. 배고파서 밥을 먹고 싶어요. 2. 저는 오늘 바빠서 시간이 없어요. 3. 공부를 안 해서/못 하지 않아서 시험에 떨어졌어요. 4. 카페에 가서 커피를 마셨어요. 5. 영화관에 가서 영화를 봤어요.

Please be aware that not all sentences have one exact translation, so answers may vary slightly.

어휘

병원에 입원한 적이 있어요?
[byeon-gwo-ne i-bwon-han jeo-gi i-sseo-yo?]

Recommended Vocabulary

병원에 입원한 적이 있어요? [Have you ever been hospitalized?]

입원하다 - to be hospitalized	병원 - a hospital	심하다 - serious/severe
퇴원하다 - to be discharged	의사 - a doctor	간호사 - a nurse

왜 병원에 입원했어요? [Why were you admitted to the hospital?]

(독감)에 걸리다 - to catch the (flu)	(장염)에 걸리다 - to have a (stomach bug)	(폐렴)에 걸리다 - to catch/get (pneumonia)
사고가 나다 - to have an accident	증상이 있다 -to have symptoms	맹장이 터지다 - one's appendix bursts
탈구되다 - to be dislocated	감염되다 - have an infection	아기를 낳다 - to have a baby
차사고 - a car accident	뇌진탕 - a concussion	골절 - a bone fracture
알레르기 - an allergy	뼈가 부러지다 - break a bone	편도염 - tonsillitis

얼마나 오랫동안 병원에 있었어요? [How long were you hospitalized?]

4일 정도 - about 4 days	2주 동안 - for 2 weeks	1박 2일 - 2 days & 1 night
이틀 - 2 days	하루 동안 - for a day	밤을 보내다 - spend a night
오래 있다 - to stay for a long time	몇 일 - a few days	몇 주 - a few weeks

어떤 치료를 받았어요? [What kind of treatment did you get?]

상처를 꿰매다 - to stitch a wound	주사를 맞다 - to get a shot/injection	처방받다 - to get a prescription
항생제 - antibiotics	진통제 - painkillers	링거를 맞다 - to get an IV
엑스레이를 찍다 - to get an x-ray	약을 먹다 -to take medicine	나아지다 - to get better
	수술을 하다 - to do surgery	깁스를 하다 - to get a cast

157

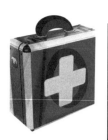

육하원칙

병원에 입원한 적이 있어요?
[byeon-gwo-ne i-bwon-han jeo-gi i-sseo-yo?]

Developing Your Answer

병원에 입원한 적이 있어요?	Have you ever been hospitalized?
네, 입원한 적이 있어요.	[Yes, I have been hospitalized.]
아니요, 입원한 적이 없어요.	[No, I haven't been hospitalized.]
장염으로 입원해 본 적이 있어요.	[I was hospitalized for a stomach bug.]
네, 교통사고 후에 병원에 입원했어요.	[Yes, I was hospitalized after a car accident.]
맹장수술로 입원해 봤어요.	[I was hospitalized for appendicitis.]

Your Turn:

왜 병원에 입원했어요?	Why were you admitted to the hospital?
뼈가 부러져서 병원에 입원했어요.	[I was hospitalized because I broke a bone.]
손목이 탈구돼서 병원에 갔어요.	[I went to the hospital when I dislocated my wrist.]
땅콩 알레르기 때문에 입원했어요.	[I was hospitalized for a peanut allergy.]
독감이 심해져서 폐렴에 걸렸어요.	[My flu was so bad that I got pneumonia.]
맹장이 터져서 맹장수술이 필요했어요.	[My appendix burst, so I needed an appendectomy.]

Your Turn:

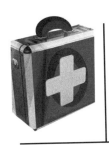

육하원칙

병원에 입원한 적이 있어요?
[byeon-gwo-ne i-bwon-han jeo-gi i-sseo-yo?]

Developing Your Answer

얼마나 오랫동안 병원에 있었어요?	How long were you hospitalized?
3일 정도 입원했어요.	[I was hospitalized for about 3 days.]
정말 아파서 병원에 오래 있어야 했어요.	[I was really sick, so I had to stay for a long time.]
수술 후에 병원에서 밤을 보냈어요.	[I spent a night in the hospital after my surgery.]
저는 사고 후 2주 동안 병원에 있었어요.	[I was in the hospital for 2 weeks after an accident.]
저는 몇 일 후에 병원에서 퇴원했어요.	[I was discharged after a few days.]

Your Turn:

어떤 치료를 받았어요?	What kind of treatment did you get?
의사는 저에게 진통제를 처방했어요.	[The doctor prescribed me painkillers.]
링거를 맞고 병원에서 쉬었어요.	[I got an IV, and rested in the hospital.]
편도염이 있어서 수술을 해야 했어요.	[I had tonsillitis, so I had to have surgery.]
저는 항생제를 먹고 천천히 나아졌어요.	[I took antibiotics and slowly got better.]
상처가 깊어서 꿰매야 했어요.	[The wound was deep, so I had to get stitches.]

Your Turn:

쓰기

병원에 입원한 적이 있어요?
[byeon-gwo-ne i-bwon-han jeo-gi i-sseo-yo?]

Try Writing Your Own Answer

1) Write your own answer below to the question -- 병원에 입원한 적이 있어요? --

2) Get your answer corrected and rewrite your corrected answer here:

You can post your writing on an app/website like *Hellotalk* or *Hinative* for free corrections.

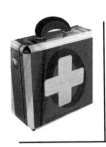

대화

병원에 입원한 적이 있어요?
[byeon-gwo-ne i-bwon-han jeo-gi i-sseo-yo?]

Example Conversation

소피: 사라씨, 뼈가 부러진 적이 있나요?
Sarah, have you ever broken a bone?

사라: 있어요. 어렸을 때 미끄럼틀에서 떨어졌어요.
I have. When I was young I fell off a slide.

소피: 아. 많이 아팠어요?
Ah. Did it hurt a lot?

사라: 사실, 처음에는 미끄럼틀에서 떨어진 게 놀래서 아픔을 못 느꼈어요. 하하 근데, 그 다음에 아프기 시작해서 많이 울었어요.
Actually, at first I was surprised from falling off the slide, so I didn't feel the pain. Haha. But after that it started to hurt, so I cried a lot.

소피: 병원에 갔어요?
Did you go to the hospital?

사라: 네, 병원에 갔어요. 다행히 입원은 하지 않았지만 6주 동안 깁스를 해야 했어요.
Yes, I went to the hospital. Fortunately I wasn't hospitalized, but I had to wear a cast for 6 months.

소피: 아, 깁스를 오래 하셨네요. 그래도 입원은 하지 않아서 다행이네요.
Oh, you had a cast for a long time. But still, at least you weren't hospitalized.

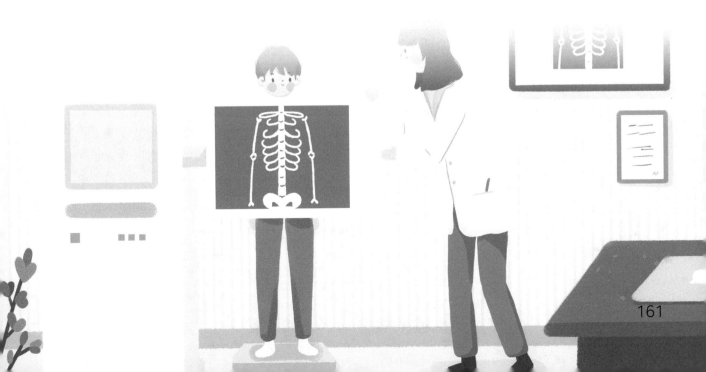

문화

병원에 입원한 적이 있어요?
[byeon-gwo-ne i-bwon-han jeo-gi i-sseo-yo?]

Culture Note

병원

South Korea's medical system is ranked #1 in the world according to CEOWorld Magazine's Health Care Index. [18] At a major Korean hospital, you can expect to receive the same quality of care you'd usually receive at a major American hospital. Most Korean doctors and nurses also speak English, particularly in Seoul. Depending on the treatment, the Korean government covers 50-90% of medical costs [5], and you can anticipate that general visits will cost less than $100, even as a foreigner with no health insurance.

Korean hospitals may operate a little differently than what you're used to. [16] One of the most prevalent differences is that one's family members usually take on some of the duties we may expect to be included in a nurse's role (an idea known as 간병). This primary caregiver role includes feeding the patient, accompanying them to the bathroom, and generally attending to their more personal needs. The hospital provides a cot next to the patient's bed specifically for family members to sleep in and use during their stay. [19]

Q16

이상형은 어떤 사람이에요?

[i-sang-hyeon-geun eo-tteon sa-ra-mi-e-yo?]

What kind of person is your ideal type?

이상형	ideal type
~은/는	topic particle
어떤	what; what kind of; which
사람	person
~이에요/예요	the copula "to be"

대답

이상형은 어떤 사람이에요?
[i-sang-hyeon-geun eo-tteon sa-ra-mi-e-yo?]
What kind of person is your ideal type?

의지하고 믿을 수 있는 사람이요!

쉬고 싶을 때 어깨를 내어 주는 사람이요.

그런 사람을 만날 수 있었으연 좋겠어요.

A person I can rely on and trust!
Someone who offers their shoulder when I want to rest (my head).
I wish I could meet a person like that.

Answer Breakdown

Vocabulary	Grammar
Nouns	~을/를 Object Particle
사람 - person	Present Tense ~아/어요
어깨 - shoulder	A/V~고
그런 - that kind of (N); a (N) like that	V~고 싶다
Action Verbs	V~(으)ㄹ 수 있다/없다
의지하다 - to rely/depend on; to lean on	V~아/어 주다
믿다 - to believe (in); to trust	V~는 N
쉬다 - to rest/relax	A/V~ㄹ/을 때, N 때
내어 주다 - give; offer up	A/V~ 았/었으면 좋겠다
만나다 - to meet	N~(이)요

The grammar is color-coded to match chapters in *Conversational Korean Grammar*.

설명

Grammar Spotlight

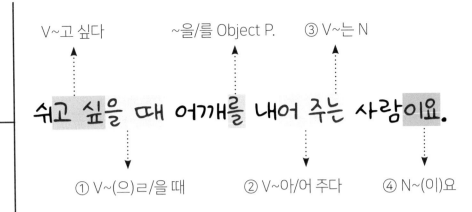

V~고 싶다

~을/를 Object P.

③ V~는 N

쉬고 싶을 때 어깨를 내어 주는 사람이요.

① V~(으)ㄹ/을 때

② V~아/어 주다

④ N~(이)요

① A/V~ㄹ/을 때: The form **~ㄹ/을 때** attaches to the stem of action verbs and descriptive verbs, and it means "the time that" or "when" that verb happens. In the example above, it combines with "쉬고 싶다" (to want to rest) to make "쉬고 싶을 **때**" (when I want to rest).

데이트 **할 때** 꽃을 받고 싶어요.　　　　I want to receive flowers when I'm on a date.

얘기 **할 때** 유머러스한 사람이 좋아요.　　When we chat, I like someone who's funny.

② A/V~아/어 주다: This form is used when you want to talk about an action that is done for the sake of someone else. It is similar to doing something (a favor) for someone else's sake. In the sentence above, the verb "내어 주다" (to give/offer up) becomes "내어 **줘요**" (I offer something to someone).

제가 피곤할 때 남친은 가방을 들**어 줘요**.　　My boyfriend holds my bag for me when I'm tired.

배고팠을 때 여친이 자주 요리**해 줬어요**.　　When I was hungry, my girlfriend cooked for me.

③ V~는 N: Use this form to change an action verb into it's present tense noun modifying (adjective) form. Place it in front of a noun to describe that noun as "a **noun** that **verb**s". The verb "내어 주다" (to give/offer up) pairs with "사람" (person), becoming "내어 주**는** 사람" (a person who offers/gives).

위로를 잘 해 주**는** 사람이 좋아요.　　　I like a person who can cheer me up.

미소를 잘 보여 주**는** 남자를 좋아해요.　　I like a guy that smiles often.

④ N~(이)요: Attached to a noun, this form simply allows you to create a complete, polite sentence with only the noun; e.g. "a noun." The example above shows "사람**이요**." (A person.)

똑똑하고 공부를 잘 하는 사람**이요**.　　Someone smart who studies well.

호탕하고 잘 먹는 사람**이요**!　　　　　A spirited person who eats well!

문법

V~(으)ㄴ/는/(으)ㄹ N
[To turn verbs into their noun-modifying forms]

Grammar Practice

V~(으)ㄴ/는/(으)ㄹ N

This form changes a verb into its adjective form. Place it right before the noun it's modifying. Use **V~(으)ㄴ** for past, **V~는** for present, and **V~(으)ㄹ** for future tense.

Scan the QR code to view a short grammar lesson PDF.

Given the English sentence below, use the grammar form above to write the equivalent expression in Korean. Including "저는" in your sentences is optional.

1. The food I'm eating now is rice.

지금 - now | 먹다 - eat | 음식 - food | 밥 - rice

....

2. A girl who likes coffee is great.

좋아하다 - to like | 여자 - girl | 좋다 - great

....

3. The movie I'm watching now is boring.

보다 - watch | 영화 - movie | 재미없다 - boring

....

4. I want to eat the pizza I made earlier.

아까 - earlier | *만들다 - make | 피자 - pizza

....

5. I'm looking for the person I will marry.

결혼하다 - marry | 사람 - person | 찾다 - look for

....

*Irregular Verb: Be aware that this verb conjugates irregularly.

ANSWERS: 1. 지금 먹는 음식은 밥이에요. 2. 커피를 좋아하는 여자가 좋아요. 3. 지금 보고 있는 영화는 재미없어요. 4. 아까 만든 피자를 먹고 싶어요. 5. 결혼할 사람을 찾고 있어요.

Please be aware that not all sentences have one exact translation, so answers may vary slightly.

어휘

이상형은 어떤 사람이에요?
[i-sang-hyeon-geun eo-tteon sa-ra-mi-e-yo?]

Recommended Vocabulary

어떤 외모가 이상형인가요? [What is your ideal type's appearance like?]

키가 크다/작다 - tall/short

보조개가 있다 - have dimples

미소 - a smile

잘생기다 - to be handsome

몸매가 좋다 - to be fit

외모 - one's appearance

문신이 있다 - to have tattoos

안경을 쓰다 - wear glasses

멋지다 - to be cool/stylish

동갑이다 - the same age

귀엽다 - to be cute

예쁘다 - to be pretty

피부가 좋다 - have good skin

머리가 짧다 - have short hair

머리가 길다 - have long hair

어떤 성격이 이상형인가요? [What is your ideal type's personality like?]

성격 - personality

착하다 - to be nice/good

재미있다 - fun; interesting

조용하다 - to be quiet

똑똑하다 - to be smart

다정하다 - affectionate

솔직하다 - honest; open

든든하다 - to be reliable

느긋하다 - to be easy-going

내성적이다 - introverted

사교적이다 - extroverted

매력이 있다 - to be charming

활발하다 - to be active/energetic

자상하다 - to be thoughtful/considerate

차분하다 - to be calm

이상형을 만나 본 적이 있어요? [Have you ever met your ideal type?]

소개팅 - a blind date

결혼하다 - to get married

친해지다 - to get closer

데이팅 앱 - a dating app

어울리다 - to suit/match

헤어지다 - to break up

짝사랑 - one-sided/unrequited love

전남친 - ex boyfriend
전여친 - ex girlfriend

사귀다 - 1) to date/go out; 2) get along with (friends)

피하고 싶은 이성의 유형이 있나요? [What are your dealbreakers?]

담배를 피다 - to smoke

거짓말을 하다 - to lie

거만하다 - to be arrogant

개인 위생이 나쁘다 - to have bad personal hygiene

무례하다 - to be rude/impolite

입냄새가 나다 - to have bad breath

167

육하원칙

이상형은 어떤 사람이에요?
[i-sang-hyeon-geun eo-tteon sa-ra-mi-e-yo?]

Developing Your Answer

어떤 외모가 이상형인가요?	What is your ideal type's appearance like?
잘 생겼고 미소가 예쁜 사람이요.	[A handsome person with a nice smile.]
몸매가 좋은 사람을 좋아해요.	[I'd like someone who's fit.]
문신하고 피어싱이 있는 사람을 좋아해요.	[I like people with piercings and tattoos.]
저는 외모는 별로 보지 않아요.	[I don't really care about appearances.]
안경을 쓰고 보조개가 있으면 좋겠어요.	[I'd like it if they wear glasses and have dimples.]

Your Turn:

어떤 성격이 이상형인가요?	What is your ideal type's personality like?
착하고 느긋한 사람이요.	[Someone with a nice and easy-going personality.]
그냥 재미있는 사람을 좋아해요!	[I just like fun people!]
자상하고 든든하면 좋겠어요.	[I'd like it if they were thoughtful and reliable.]
저 같이 사교적이고 활발한 사람이요.	[Someone out-going and energetic like me.]
차분하고 조용한 사람을 선호해요.	[I prefer calm, quiet people.]

Your Turn:

168

육하원칙

이상형은 어떤 사람이에요?
[i-sang-hyeon-geun eo-tteon sa-ra-mi-e-yo?]

Developing Your Answer

이상형을 만나 본 적이 있어요?	Have you ever met your ideal type?
네! 저는 이상형을 만나서 결혼했어요.	[Yes! I already met and married my ideal type.]
아니요, 아직 그런 사람을 못 만나 봤어요.	[No, I haven't met someone like that yet.]
최근에 데이팅 앱에서 제 이상형을 만났어요.	[I recently met my ideal type through a dating app.]
소개팅에서 만났지만 짝사랑으로 끝났어요.	[I met them on a blind date, but it was one-sided.]
전 남친이 이상형이었지만 헤어졌어요.	[My ex-bf was my ideal type, but we broke up.]

Your Turn:

피하고 싶은 이성의 유형이 있나요?	What are your dealbreakers?
섬원들에게 무례한 사람을 완전 싫어해요.	[I totally hate people who are rude to employees.]
거만한 사람들은 짜증나요.	[Arrogant people are annoying.]
그 사람을 믿을 수 없다면 헤어져야 해요.	[If I can't trust them, we have to break up.]
담배를 피거나 입냄새가 나면 안 돼요.	[They can't smoke or have bad breath.]
애인이 나에게 거짓말하는 것은 안 돼요.	[My partner can't lie to me.]

Your Turn:

쓰기

이상형은 어떤 사람이에요?
[i-sang-hyeon-geun eo-tteon sa-ra-mi-e-yo?]

Try Writing Your Own Answer

1) Write your own answer below to the question   -- 이상형은 어떤 사람이에요? --

2) Get your answer corrected and rewrite your corrected answer here:

You can post your writing on an app/website like *Hellotalk* or *Hinative* for free corrections.

대화

이상형은 어떤 사람이에요?
[i-sang-hyeon-geun eo-tteon sa-ra-mi-e-yo?]

Example Conversation

소피: 희진 언니, 이상형은 어떤 사람이에요?

Heejin, what kind of person is your ideal type?

희진: 흠... 착하고 자기관리를 잘 **하는** 사람이에요. 소피는요?

Hm... a person who's nice and takes care of themself. What about you, Sophie?

소피: 키가 크고 어깨도 넓었으면 좋겠어요. 그리고 미소가 예쁜 사람이요!

I'd like it if they're tall and have broad shoulders. And someone with a nice smile!

희진: 아, 네 그럼 대박이겠네요. 하하 그런 사람을 사귀어 본 적이 있어요?

Oh, yeah that would be great. Haha. Have you ever dated someone like that?

소피: 저는 없어요. 희진 언니는요?

I haven't. How about you, Heejin?

희진: 네, 저는 제 이상형을 소개팅에서 만나 봤어요. 그런데 잘 풀리지는 않았어요.

Yes, I met my ideal type on a blind date. But in the end it just didn't work out.

소피: 아쉽네요.

That's too bad.

희진: 그런 사람을 다시 만날 수 있으면 좋겠어요.

I hope I can meet someone like that again.

소피: 저도 언젠간 제 이상형을 만나 보고 싶어요.

I want to meet my ideal type someday too.

문화

이상형은 어떤 사람이에요?
[i-sang-hyeon-geun eo-tteon sa-ra-mi-e-yo?]

Culture Note

미팅

Korea has a long history of matchmaking. Due to strong Confucian values, men and women were not allowed to mingle freely in the past, and instead used matchmakers to find suitable partners. [22]

While formal matchmaking is less common now, it's still very common for friends, parents, or relatives to set up meetings (미팅) and blind dates (소개팅) between people they believe would be a good match. Typically, a person arranges for some of their single friends to get together as a group ("미팅"), or one-on-one for a blind date ("소개팅"). Parents and relatives may also arrange 소개팅 for their children, nieces and nephews, etc.

People usually meet at a cafe or bar, and if things go well, participants can exchange contact information and pursue a relationship from there. Speed dating ("번개팅") and online dating ("온라인 데이트") are also common.

Q17

어떤 것을 가르칠 수 있어요?

[eo-tteon geo-seul ga-reu-chil su i-sseo-yo?]

What can you teach?

어떤	: what; what kind of; which
것	: thing, object, item
~을/를	: object particle
가르치다	: to teach
V~(으)ㄹ 수 있다	: used to talk about ability; "can"
~아/어요	: informal polite present tense

대답

어떤 것을 가르칠 수 있어요?

[eo-tteon geo-seul ga-reu-chil su i-sseo-yo?]

What can you teach?

저는 피아노를 칠 줄 알아요.
그래서 아이들에게 피아노를 가르칠 수 있을 것 같아요.
하지만 잘 가르칠 수 있을지는 잘 모르겠어요.

I know how to play the piano.
So I think I could teach the piano to children.
But I don't really know if I could teach it well.

Answer Breakdown

Vocabulary	Grammar
Nouns	~은/는 Topic Particle
저 - I; me	~을/를 Object Particle
피아노 - piano	A/V~아/어요 Present Tense
그래서 - So/Therefore (sentence starter)	N~들
아이 - a kid; a child	그리고, 그래서 & 하지만
하지만 - But/However (sentence starter)	잘 & 잘 못
Action Verbs	N~께/에게/한테
피아노를 치다 - to play the piano	V~(으)ㄹ 수 있다/없다
가르치다 - to teach	V~(으)ㄹ 줄 알다/모르다
모르다 - to not know	V~(은/는/을) 것 같다
	A/V~(으)ㄴ/는/~(으)ㄹ지
	A/V~겠다

The grammar is color-coded to match chapters in *Conversational Korean Grammar*.

설명

Grammar Spotlight

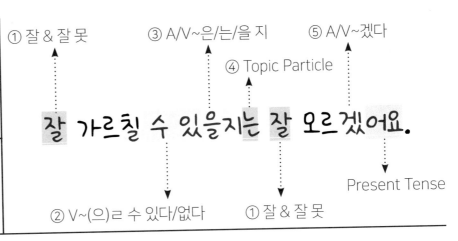

① 잘 & 잘 못

③ A/V~은/는/을 지

⑤ A/V~겠다

④ Topic Particle

잘 가르칠 수 있을지는 잘 오르겠어요.

② V~(으)ㄹ 수 있다/없다

① 잘 & 잘 못

Present Tense

① **잘 & 잘 못:** 잘 means "well" or "good". It is an adverb that's used to describe **how** an action is done, and it appears before action verbs. eg: "**잘** 가르쳐요." (I teach well). When used the second time above as "**잘** 모르겠어요", it means something like "I don't really know."

저는 기타를 **잘 못** 쳐요.   I'm not good at playing the guitar.

그건 **잘** 모르겠어요.   I don't really know about that.

② **V~(으)ㄹ 수 있다/없다:** This form attaches to action verb stems, and is used to talk about ability. Attach **~(으)ㄹ 수 있다** to say "I can do..." and **~(으)ㄹ 수 없다** to say "I can't do..." In the example above, "가르치다" (to teach) becomes "가르**칠 수 있어요**" (I can teach).

피아노를 잘 **칠 수 있어요**.   I can play the piano well.

일본어를 잘 못 해서 가르**칠 수 없어요**.   I'm bad at Japanese, so I can't teach it.

③ **A/V~(으)ㄴ/는/~(으)ㄹ지:** This form attaches to a verb to indicate uncertainty "if/whether" something is true. As shown above, "가르칠 수 있다" (to be able to teach) becomes "가르칠 수 있**을지**" (whether/if I can teach). It is usually followed by verbs like "모르다" (to not know), "궁금하다" (curious), "확실하다" (certain), "물어보다" (to ask), etc.

피아노를 배울 수 있**을지** 모르겠어요.   I don't know if I'll be able to learn the piano.

유치원생은 가르칠 수 없**을지**도 몰라요.   I might not be able to teach kindergarteners.

④ **~은/는 Topic Particle:** the topic particle is here to add emphasis.

⑤ **V~겠다:** ~겠다 has a few uses. but here it simply raises the politeness of the verb "모르다" (to not know). "모르**겠어요**" is more polite than "몰라요," though they mean the same thing.

대학교에서 강의 할 수 있을지 모르**겠어요**.   I don't know if I'd be able to lecture at a university.

온라인 강의를 할 수 있을지 잘 모르**겠어요**.   I don't know if I'd be able to teach online.

문법

V~(으)ㄹ 줄 알다/모르다
[To talk about things that you've learned]

Grammar Practice

V~(으)ㄹ 줄 알다/모르다

Attach this form to action verbs. Use **~(으)ㄹ 줄 알다** to say "(subject) knows how to (verb)." Use **~(으)ㄹ 줄 모르다** to say "(subject) doesn't know how to (verb)."

Scan the QR code to view a short grammar lesson PDF.

Given the English sentence below, use the grammar form above to write the equivalent expression in Korean. Including "저는" in your sentences is optional.

1. I know how to make pasta.

파스타 - pasta | 만들다 - make

....

2. I don't know how to get there.

거기 - there | 가다 - go

....

3. I know how to speak Korean.

한국어 - Korean | 하다 - do/speak

....

4. I don't know how to drive a car.

차 - car | 운전하다 - drive

....

5. I know how to use chopsticks.

젓가락 - chopsticks | 쓰다 - use

....

ANSWERS: 1. 저는 파스타를 만들 줄 알아요. 2. 저는 거기에 갈 줄 몰라요. 3. 저는 한국어를 할 줄 알아요. 4. 저는 차를 운전할 줄 몰라요. 5. 저는 젓가락을 쓸 줄 알아요.

Please be aware that not all sentences have one exact translation, so answers may vary slightly.

어휘

어떤 것을 가르칠 수 있어요?
[eo-tteon geo-seul ga-reu-chil su i-sseo-yo?]

Recommended Vocabulary

어떤 것을 가르칠 수 있어요? [What can you teach?]

수학 - math	언어 - a language	운전하는 법 - how to drive
요리하는 법 - how to cook	노래하는 법 - how to sing	가르치다 - to teach
체육 - physical education	영어 문법 - English grammar	역사 - history
악기를 연주하다 - to play an instrument	수영하는 법 - how to swim	컴퓨터 - a computer
글씨 쓰기 - handwriting	기타 - a guitar	영문학 - English literature

가르칠 대상이 누구인가요? [Who would you teach?]

아이 - a kid; a child	어른 - an adult	부모님 - parents
중학생 - a middle school student	고등학생 - a high school student	초등학생 - an elementary school student
어르신 - a senior citizen	대학생 - a college student	유치원생 - a kindergartner

어떻게 배웠어요? [How did you learn it?]

전공하다 - to major (in)	초등학교 - an elementary school	중학교 - a middle school
고등학교 - a high school	대학교 - a college/university	독학 - self-study
혼자(서) - alone; by oneself	동아리 - a school club	모임 - a meeting/gathering
다니다 - to attend	가입하다 - to join	인터넷 - the Internet

가르치는 것을 좋아해요? [Do you like teaching?]

어렵다 - to be difficult/hard	힘들다 - difficult; hard; tiring	재미있다 - fun; interesting
의미 있다 - to be meaningful	기회가 생기다 - to have the chance	쉽다 - to be easy/simple

177

육하원칙

어떤 것을 가르칠 수 있어요?
[eo-tteon geo-seul ga-reu-chil su i-sseo-yo?]

Developing Your Answer

어떤 것을 가르칠 수 있어요?	What can you teach?
수학을 가르칠 수 있을 것 같아요.	[I think I can teach math.]
영어 문법을 가르칠 수 있을 거예요.	[I would be able to teach English grammar.]
가르칠 수 있는 게 없을 것 같아요.	[I'm not sure there's anything I can teach.]
제 특별 레시피를 가르칠 수 있어요.	[I can teach my own special (cooking) recipes.]
운전을 잘 가르칠 수 있을 것 같아요.	[I think I could teach driving well.]

Your Turn:

가르칠 대상이 누구인가요?	Who would you teach?
초등학생에게 영어를 가르칠 거예요.	[I'll teach English to elementary school kids.]
엄마들을 대상으로 요리를 가르치고 싶어요.	[I want to teach cooking to moms.]
어르신들에게 컴퓨터를 가르 칠 거예요.	[I'll teach seniors how to use computers.]
십대들에게 노래하는 법을 가르칠 수 있어요.	[I could teach teenagers how to sing.]
유치원생한테 글씨 쓰기를 가르치고 싶어요.	[I want to teach kindergarteners to write.]

Your Turn:

육하원칙

어떤 것을 가르칠 수 있어요?
[eo-tteon geo-seul ga-reu-chil su i-sseo-yo?]

Developing Your Answer

어떻게 배웠어요?	How did you learn it?
저는 독학으로 배웠어요.	[I learned it through self study.]
대학교에서 영문학을 전공했어요.	[I majored in English literature at college.]
고등학교에서 기타 동아리였어요.	[I was in a guitar club in high school.]
엄마에게 요리하는 법을 배웠어요.	[I learned how to cook from my mom.]
부모님에게 운전하는 법을 배웠어요.	[I learned how to drive from my parents.]

Your Turn:

가르치는 것을 좋아해요?	Do you like teaching?
아니요, 가르치는 것은 너무 어려워요.	[No, teaching is too difficult.]
가르치는 건 의미 있지만 쉽진 않아요.	[Teaching is meaningful, but it's not easy.]
기회가 생긴다면 한번 가르쳐 보고 싶어요!	[If I had the chance, I'd like to give teaching a try!]
요즘 시간이 없어서 가르칠 수 없어요.	[These days I have no time, so I can't teach.]
어린이보다 어른들을 가르치고 싶어요.	[I'd rather teach adults than kids.]

Your Turn:

쓰기

어떤 것을 가르칠 수 있어요?
[eo-tteon geo-seul ga-reu-chil su i-sseo-yo?]

Try Writing Your Own Answer

1) Write your own answer below to the question -- 어떤 것을 가르칠 수 있어요? --

2) Get your answer corrected and rewrite your corrected answer here:

You can post your writing on an app/website like *Hellotalk* or *Hinative* for free corrections.

대화

어떤 것을 가르칠 수 있어요?
[eo-tteon geo-seul ga-reu-chil su i-sseo-yo?]

Example Conversation

소피: 보라씨, 만약에 어떤 것을 가르쳐야 한다면 무엇을 가르칠 거예요?
Bora, if you had to teach something, what would you teach?

보라: 저는 일본어를 **할 줄 알아**서 일본어를 가르칠 수 있을 것 같아요. 소피씨는요?
I know how to speak Japanese, so I think I could teach Japanese. How about you?

소피: 영어를 배우는 사람에게 영어를 가르치는 게 재미있을 것 같아요.
I think it would be fun to teach English to English learners.

보라: 그럼 학원에서 한국 아이들에게 영어를 가르치는 게 어때요?
Then how about teaching English to Korean children at a tutoring center?

소피: 아이들보다는 어른들에게 가르치는 것이 더 좋을 것 같아요...
I think teaching adults is a little better than teaching children...

보라: 왜요?
Why?

소피: 아이들에게 가르치는 건 괜찮지만 아이들은 종종 공부하기 싫어해서요. 어른들은 본인들이 배우고 싶어하는 사람들이 오기 때문에 가르치는 게 조금 더 편해요.
Teaching kids is alright, but sometimes kids don't like studying. Adults come to class because they themselves want to learn, so it's a little easier to teach them.

보라: 아, 동의해요.
Ah, I agree.

문화

어떤 것을 가르칠 수 있어요?
[eo-tteon geo-seul ga-reu-chil su i-sseo-yo?]

Culture Note

학원

Korean parents are passionate about education, and strive to provide their children with the best education possible. Many school children receive education not only in their mandatory day-school, but also in the evenings, when they go to private academies and cram schools, otherwise referred to as hagwon (학원). [35]

Hagwons (학원) are private academies that offer classes outside of regular school hours. At hagwons, students can take extra lessons in all sorts of subjects like English, Chinese, math, piano, ballet, swimming, and more. More than 83 percent of 5-year-olds attend at least one hagwon, attending 5.2 times a week on average. [34]

English hagwons are a big source of foreign employment in Korea, as they often hire foreign workers (e.g. native English speakers from the US, Canada, Australia, etc.) to provide English language immersion for their students. In 2017, there were about 15,000 people with Foreign Language Instructor visas (E2 visas) in Korea [8]. While providing a salary, many language schools also sponsor visas and provide foreign teachers with housing and health care, so it is a popular and accessible way to experience living in Korea.

Q18

여름에 즐겨하는 것이 뭐예요?

[yeo-reum-e jeul-gyeo-ha-neun-geo-si mwo-e-yo?]

What do you enjoy doing in the summer?

여름 : summer	
~에 : prepositional time particle	
즐겨하다 : to enjoy	
V~는 N : present tense noun-modifying (adjective) form	
것 : thing, object, item	
~이/가 : subject particle	
뭐 : what	
~이에요/예요 : the copula "to be"	

대답

여름에 즐거하는 것이 뭐예요?

[yeo-reum-e jeul-gyeo-ha-neun-geo-si mwo-e-yo?]

What do you enjoy doing in the summer?

여름은 덥기 때문에 집에 있는 게 좋아요.

집에서 쉬면서 그냥 뒹굴뒹굴하고 싶어요.

게으른 여름이 최고예요.

It's hot in the summer, so I like to stay home.
I want to just laze around while I relax at home.
Lazy summers are the best.

Answer Breakdown

Vocabulary	Grammar
Nouns	~은/는 Topic Particle
여름 - summer	~이/가 Subject Particle
집 - house/home	N~에 V
그냥 - just; only; simply	V~는 것
최고 - the best; the top	Present Tense ~아/어요
Action Verbs	N~에서
쉬다 - to rest/relax	N~이에요/예요
뒹굴뒹굴하다 - to laze/roll around; to idle	V~고 싶다
Descriptive Verbs	A~ㄴ/은/는 N
덥다 - to be hot	A/V~기 때문에
있다 - to exist; to have	V~(으)면서, N(이)면서
좋다 - to be good; likeable	
게으르다 - to be lazy	

The grammar is color-coded to match chapters in *Conversational Korean Grammar*.

설명

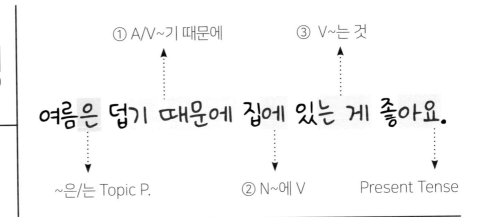

① A/V~기 때문에

③ V~는 것

여름은 덥기 때문에 집에 있는 게 좋아요.

~은/는 Topic P.

② N~에 V

Present Tense

① A/V~기 때문에: When attached to the verb stem, this form can be used to give a reason, meaning something like "because of verb" in English. In the example shown above, it attaches to 덥다, making "덥기 때문에" (because it's hot, ...). This form can also be used to end a sentence. if it were to be used at the end of a sentence, the example above would become "덥기 때문이에요" (because it's hot).

습하**기 때문에** 밖에 잘 안 나가요.   I don't really go outside because it's humid.
여름은 비가 많이 오**기 때문에** 안 좋아해요.   I don't like summer because it rains a lot.

② N~에 V: The prepositional particle **~에** attaches to a noun, and usually means something similar to the English prepositions "in/at/on." It is usually used with movement verbs like "가다/오다", but it can also be paired with existence verbs like "있다/없다." The example above pairs **~에** with the verb "있다"(to exist/be), making "집**에** 있어요" (I'm at home).

비가 오기 때문에 집**에** 있어요.   I'm at home because it's raining.
덥기 때문에 호수**에** 뛰어들었어요.   I jumped in the lake because it was hot.

③ V~는 것: Attach **~는 것** to the verb stem of an action verb to use it as a noun in your sentence. The verb used above, "있다" becomes the noun "있**는 것**" (existing/having). You can now talk about the characteristics of "existing/having" as you would any other noun. When combined with the ~이/가 subject particle, **~는 것이** often contracts to the short form **~는 게**.

수영 학원에 다니**는 것은** 재미있어요.   Going to swimming classes is fun.
여름에 감기에 걸리**는 것은** 최악이에요.   Catching a cold in the summer is the worst.

문법

A/V~기 때문에
[To talk about cause and effect]

Grammar Practice

A/V~기 때문에
Use this form to connect two clauses to say something happens "because" of something else. Attach **~기 때문에** to the verb stem at the end of the first clause.

Scan the QR code to view a short grammar lesson PDF.

Given the English sentence below, use the grammar form above to write the equivalent expression in Korean. Including "저는" in your sentences is optional.

1. I want to swim because it's hot.　　　　덥다 - hot | 수영하다 - swim

....

2. I camped because the weather was nice.　　날씨 - weather | 좋다 - nice | 캠핑을 가다 - camp

....

3. I didn't wash my face because I was tired.　피곤하다 - tired | 세수하다 - wash (one's face)

....

4. I don't have time because I'm studying.　　공부하다 - study | 시간 - time | 없다 - not have

....

5. I can't go home because I'm working.　　　일하다 - work | 집 - home | 가다 - go

....

ANSWERS: 1. 덥기 때문에 수영하고 싶어요. 2. 날씨가 좋기 때문에 캠핑을 갔어요. 3. 피곤하기 때문에 세수하지 않았어요/세수를 안 했어요. 4. 공부하기 때문에 시간이 없어요. 5. 일하기 때문에 집에 못 가요/갈 수 없어요.

Please be aware that not all sentences have one exact translation, so answers may vary slightly.

어휘

여름에 즐겨하는 것이 뭐예요?
[yeo-reum-e jeul-gyeo-ha-neun-geo-si mwo-e-yo?]

Recommended Vocabulary

여름에 즐겨하는 것이 뭐예요? [What do you enjoy doing during summer?]

수영하다 - to swim	캠핑하다 - to camp	등산하다 - to hike
여행을 하다 - to travel	밖에 가다 - to go outside	음악 축제 - a music festival
소풍을 가다 - to picnic	야외 영화를 보다 - to watch an outdoor movie	바비큐 파티를 열다 - to have a barbeque
낚시를 하다 - to fish	카누를 타다 - to canoe	자동차 여행 - a road trip
자전거를 타다 - to ride a bike	스포츠를 하다 - to play sports	불꽃놀이를 구경하다 - to watch fireworks

누구하고 함께 해요? [Who do you enjoy it with?]

가족 - family	친구 - a friend	부모님 - parents
애인 - a partner; a lover	남자친구 - a boyfriend	여자친구 - a girlfriend
강아지 - a dog/puppy	친척 - a relative	동료 - a colleague/coworker

어디로 갈 수 있어요? [Where can you go?]

수영장 - a swimming pool	해변 - the beach	산 - a mountain
야영장 - campgrounds	다른 나라 - other country	강 - a river
공원 - a park	호수 - a lake	집 - house/home
놀이공원 - a theme park	국립공원 - a national park	동물원 - a zoo

여름을 좋아해요? [Do you like summer?]

덥다 - to be hot	건조하다 - to be dry	습하다 - to be humid
따뜻하다 - to be warm	맑다 - to be sunny/clear	피하다 - to avoid
해가 길다 - the days are long	즐기다 - to enjoy	비가 많이 오다 - to rain a lot

육하원칙

여름에 즐겨하는 것이 뭐예요?
[yeo-reum-e jeul-gyeo-ha-neun-geo-si mwo-e-yo?]

Developing Your Answer

여름에 즐겨하는 것이 뭐예요?	What do you enjoy doing during summer?
이번 여름에는 바다 수영을 해 보고 싶어요.	[I want to swim in the ocean this summer.]
저는 등산하는 걸 좋아해요.	[I like to go hiking.]
여름마다 카누를 타러 강릉에 가요.	[I go to Gang-neung every summer to go canoeing.]
집순이라서 주로 집에 있어요.	[I'm a homebody, so I mostly stay home.]
자주 공원에 가서 자전거를 타요.	[I often go to the park and ride my bike.]

Your Turn:

....

....

....

누구하고 함께 해요?	Who do you enjoy it with?
가족이랑 해외 여행을 가요.	[I go on an overseas trip with my family.]
친구들이랑 자동차여행을 하려고 해요.	[I'm planning to go on a road trip with my friends.]
남자친구랑 자동차 영화관을 갈 거예요.	[I'm going to a drive-in theater with my boyfriend.]
강아지랑 해변에서 산책했으면 좋겠어요.	[I'd like to walk with my dog on the beach.]
직장 동료들이랑 야유회를 갈 거예요.	[I'll go to a company picnic with my coworkers.]

Your Turn:

....

....

....

육하원칙

여름에 즐겨하는 것이 뭐예요?
[yeo-reum-e jeul-gyeo-ha-neun-geo-si mwo-e-yo?]

Developing Your Answer

어디로 갈 수 있어요?	Where can you go?
놀이공원에서 재미있게 놀아요.	[I have fun at the theme park.]
아버지랑 호수에 가서 같이 낚시를 해요.	[I go with my dad to the lake and we fish together.]
한강에서 불꽃놀이를 구경할 수 있어요.	[I can see the fireworks at the Han River.]
국립공원에서 캠핑을 하고 싶어요.	[I want to go camping at a national park.]
가끔 동물을 보러 동물원에 가요.	[Sometimes I go to the zoo to see the animals.]

Your Turn:

여름을 좋아해요?	Do you like summer?
네, 여름에는 할 수 있는 게 많아요.	[Yes, there's lots of things to do in the summer.]
아니요, 여름은 너무 덥고 습해서 싫어요.	[No, summer's too hot and humid, so I don't like it.]
물이 따뜻해서 수영을 자주 할 수 있어요.	[The water is warm, so I can go swimming often.]
아니요, 여름보다 가을을 훨씬 더 좋아해요.	[No, I like fall way more than summer.]
네! 여름은 제가 가장 좋아하는 계절이에요.	[Yes! Summer is my favorite season.]

Your Turn:

189

여름에 즐겨하는 것이 뭐예요?

[yeo-reum-e jeul-gyeo-ha-neun-geo-si mwo-e-yo?]

Try Writing Your Own Answer

1) Write your own answer below to the question   -- 여름에 즐겨하는 것이 뭐예요? --

2) Get your answer corrected and rewrite your corrected answer here:

You can post your writing on an app/website like *Hellotalk* or *Hinative* for free corrections.

대화

여름에 즐겨하는 것이 뭐예요?
[yeo-reum-e jeul-gyeo-ha-neun-geo-si mwo-e-yo?]

Example Conversation

메리: 서윤씨, 여름에 즐겨하는 것이 뭐예요?
Seoyoon, what do you enjoy doing during the summer?

서윤: 저는 여행을 좋아하는 사람이에요. 하지만 항상 여행을 가는 것은 비싸서 가끔은 호캉스 가는 것을 선호해요.
I'm the type who likes to take trips. But traveling all the time is expensive, so sometimes I prefer to have a staycation.

메리: 호캉스의 가장 좋은 점은 무엇이에요?
What's the best part about a staycation?

서윤: 멀리 가지 않아도 되**기 때문에** 좋은 것 같아요. 그냥 집에서 마음에 드는 호텔을 정해서 앱으로 쉽게 예약해서 가면 돼요.
I think it's nice because you don't have to go far. You just choose a hotel you like right from your house, book it easily with an app, and go.

메리: 아, 정말 간단하네요. 저도 한번 해 보고 싶어요.
Oh, that's really simple. I'd like to try it sometime.

서윤: 맞아요. 저는 강력 추천해요. 편하고 가격도 여행을 가는 것보다 훨씬 저렴해요.
Totally. I highly recommend it. It's convenient and it's way cheaper than a big trip.

문화

여름에 즐겨하는 것이 뭐예요?
[yeo-reum-e jeul-gyeo-ha-neun-geo-si mwo-e-yo?]

Culture Note

호캉스

Korean people usually have around 15 days of vacation per year, and most people take their vacation around the same time: the end of July and the start of August [23]. This causes a flood of both domestic and international tourism at this time of year (known as summer vacation, or 여름방학). Popular travel destinations include China, Japan, and Vietnam, because they offer quick flights and travel packages catering to Korean tourists.

However, instead of taking the trouble to book a big trip like this (which is likely to be crowded and expensive), a popular new trend for holiday travel is to stay at a "hokangsu" (호캉스) instead. The word "hokangsu" is a combination of the words 'hotel' and 'vacance' (French for 'vacation'). Staying at a hokangsu is similar to having a "staycation." Instead of going on a big trip, you just quickly and easily book someplace you like nearby, and enjoy a quick getaway and a well-deserved break there instead.

Q19

영화를 보면 자주 울어요?

[yeong-hwa-reul bo-myeon ja-ju u-reo-yo?]

Do you often cry when you watch movies?

영화 : movie, film

~을/를 : object particle

보다 : to see/watch

~면 : conditional "if/when"

자주 : often

울다 : to cry

~아/어요 : informal polite present tense

대답

영화를 보면 자주 울어요?
[yeong-hwa-reul bo-myeon ja-ju u-reo-yo?]
Do you often cry when you watch movies?

아니요, 영화를 보면서 운 적이 없어요.
어렸을 때부터 눈물이 없는 편이거든요.
평소에도 잘 울지 않아요.

No, I've never cried while watching a movie.
Ever since I was young, I haven't really been the type to cry.
Ordinarilly I don't cry much.

Answer Breakdown

Vocabulary	Grammar
Nouns	~을/를 Object Particle
아니요 - no	~이/가 Subject Particle
영화 - movie	A/V~아/어요 Present Tense
눈물 - tears	A/V~았/었다 Past Tense
평소에 - ordinarilly; usually; normally	N~부터 & N~까지
Action Verbs	N~도
보다 - to see/watch	A/V~지 않다
울다 - to cry	보통, 주로 & 평소에
Descriptive Verbs	잘 & 잘 못 V
어리다 - to be young	V~(으)면서, N(이)면서
없다 - to not exist; to not have	V~(으)ㄴ 적이 있다/없다
	A/V~ㄹ/을 때, N 때
	A/V~(으)ㄴ/는 편이다
	A/V~거든(요), N(이)거든요

The grammar is color-coded to match chapters in *Conversational Korean Grammar*.

설명

Grammar Spotlight

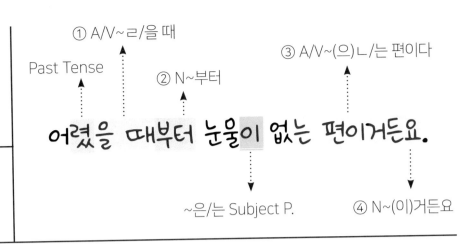

① A/V ~ㄹ/을 때
Past Tense

② N ~부터

③ A/V ~(으)ㄴ/는 편이다

어렸을 때부터 눈물이 없는 편이거든요.

~은/는 Subject P.

④ N ~(이)거든요

① A/V~ㄹ/을 때: The form **~ㄹ/을 때** attaches to the stem of action verbs and descriptive verbs, and it means "the time that" or "when" that verb happens. When referring to a time in the past, the past tense form **~았/었을 때** can be used. In the example above, it combines with "어리다" (to be young) in the past tense, making "어렸을 때..." (when I was young...)

영화를 **볼 때** 팝콘을 먹어요.	I eat popcorn when I watch movies.
공포영화를 **볼 때** 무섭지 않아요.	I'm not scared when I watch horror movies.

② N~부터: This particle is used to talk about a range of time. It is similar to the way "from" or "since" are used to talk about time in English. In the sentence above, "어렸을 때 (when I was young) combines with **~부터**, creating "어렸을 때**부터**" (from when/since I was young).

어렸을 때**부터** 애니메이션을 좋아했어요.	I've liked animated movies since I was young.
대학교 때**부터** 한국 드라마를 좋아했어요.	I've liked Korean dramas ever since college.

③ A/V~(으)ㄴ/는 편이다: This form attaches to the verb stem showing a tendency to be some way or do some action. It adds the softening nuance of "rather/fairly/pretty." In the example above, it attaches to "눈물이 없다," (to not cry), making "눈물이 없**는 편이에요**" (I tend to not cry).

어렸을 때부터 눈물이 많**은 편이에요**.	Ever since I was young, I've always cried easily.
대학교 때부터 영화를 자주 안 보**는 편이에요**.	I haven't really watched movies since college.

④ N~(이)거든요: When attached to a noun, **~(이)거든요** has the meaning "because/since". In the example above, this form attaches to the noun "편" (side) in "울지 않는 편이다" (to tend to not cry), becoming "울지 않는 편**이거든요**" (because I don't tend to cry).

주 중에 바빠서 주말에 드라마를 몰아보는 편**이거든요**.	During the week I'm busy, so I tend to binge watch dramas on the weekend.
말리와 나라는 영화를 보면서 펑펑 울었어요. 강아지가 죽는 장면이 너무 슬펐**거든요**.	I cried my eyes out while watching "Marley and Me." Because the scene where the dog dies was so sad.

문법

A/V~(으)ㄴ/는 편이다
[To talk about they way things tend to be]

Grammar Practice

A/V~(으)ㄴ/는 편이다

Use this form to say something "tends to happen" or "tends to be." Attach **~(으)ㄴ 편이다** to descriptive verbs. Attach **~는 편이다** to all action verbs.

Scan the QR code to view a short grammar lesson PDF.

Given the English sentence below, use the grammar form above to write the equivalent expression in Korean. Including "저는" in your sentences is optional.

1. Mary is pretty good at studying.

메리 - Mary | 공부 - studying | 잘 하다 - do well

....

2. My younger brother is on the tall side.

남동생 - younger brother | 키가 크다 - tall

....

3. I go swimming fairly often.

수영하다 - swim | 자주 - often

....

4. I tend to eat spicy foods pretty well.

*맵다 - spicy | 음식 - food | 잘 먹다 - to eat well

....

5. That test was on the easy side.

그 시험 - that test | *쉽다 - easy

....

*Irregular Verb: Be aware that this verb conjugates irregularly.

ANSWERS: 1. 메리는 공부를 잘 하는 편이에요. 2. 제 남동생은 키가 큰 편이에요. 3. 저는 수영을 자주 하는 편이에요. 4. 저는 매운 음식을 잘 먹는 편이에요. 5. 그 시험은 쉬운 편이었어요.

Please be aware that not all sentences have one exact translation, so answers may vary slightly.

어휘

영화를 보면 자주 울어요?
[yeong-hwa-reul bo-myeon ja-ju u-reo-yo?]

Recommended Vocabulary

영화를 보면서 울어본 적이 있어요? [Have you ever cried watching a movie?]

가끔 - sometimes	자주 - often	항상 - always
절대 (+ negative) - never	별로 (+ negative) - not really	쉽다 - to be easy/simple
영화를 보다 - watch a movie	울다 - to cry	웃다 - to laugh
슬프다 - to be sad	재미있다 - fun; interesting	웃기다 - to be funny

영화의 어떤 부분이 울게 했나요? [What part of the movie made you cry?]

첫 부분 - the beginning	중간 부분 - the middle	마지막 부분 - the end
배우 - an actor	표현 - facial expressions	표현하다 - to express
장면 - a scene	캐릭터의 감정 - the character's emotions/feelings	줄거리 - the plot; storyline
모습 - form; image	펑펑 울다 - to cry hard	눈물이 나다 - to tear up

마지막으로 울었던 영화가 언제예요? [When was the last movie you cried at?]

작년 - last year	지난 달 - last month	지난 주 - last week
이번 달 - this month	이번 주 - this week	올해 - this year
몇 달 전 - a few months ago	몇 주 전 - a few weeks ago	몇 년 전 - a few years ago
주말 - weekend	최근 - recently	오래 되다 - to be a while

슬픈 영화를 좋아해요? [Do you like sad movies?]

슬픈 영화 - a sad movie	공포 영화 - a horror movie	액션 영화 - an action movie
코미디 영화 - a comedy movie	감정이입을 하다 - to empathize	멜로 영화 - a romance movie

육하원칙

영화를 보면 자주 울어요?
[yeong-hwa-reul bo-myeon ja-ju u-reo-yo?]

Developing Your Answer

영화를 보면서 울어본 적이 있어요?	Have you ever cried watching a movie?
네, 슬픈 영화를 보면 자주 우는 편이에요.	[Yes, I cry fairly often when I watch sad movies.]
아니요, 영화를 보면서 운 적이 없어요.	[No, I've never cried while watching a movie.]
사실 저는 웃긴 영화만 봐서 없어요.	[Actually I only watch funny movies, so I haven't.]
아니요, 책을 읽으면서 운 적은 있어요.	[No, I've cried while reading a book.]
슬프지 않은 영화를 봐도 가끔 울어요.	[Sometimes I even cry watching movies that aren't sad.]

Your Turn:

영화의 어떤 부분이 울게 했나요?	What part of the movie made you cry?
영화의 마지막 부분에 슬픈 장면 많았어요.	[There were lots of sad scenes at the end.]
배우가 캐릭터의 감정을 잘 표현했어요.	[The actor expressed the characters emotions well.]
"Up"의 시작부가 너무 슬퍼서 울었어요.	[The beginning of "Up" was so sad that I cried.]
배우의 우는 모습만 봐도 눈물이 났어요.	[I teared up just seeing the actor cry.]
펑펑 울진 않았지만 눈물이 조금 났어요.	[I didn't cry my eyes out, but I teared up a bit.]

Your Turn:

육하원칙

영화를 보면 자주 울어요?
[yeong-hwa-reul bo-myeon ja-ju u-reo-yo?]

Developing Your Answer

마지막으로 울었던 영화가 언제예요?	When was the last movie you cried at?
영화를 보면서 운지 1년쯤 됐어요.	[It's been about a year since I cried watching a movie.]
작년에 본 영화는 너무 슬펐어요.	[One movie I saw last year was really sad.]
"타이타닉" 이후로는 안 울어 봤어요.	[I haven't cried since I saw "Titanic".]
최근에 슬픈 영화를 봤지만 울진 않았어요.	[I watched a sad movie recently, but I didn't cry.]
슬픈 영화를 본지 오래됐어요.	[It's been a long time since I watched a sad movie.]

Your Turn:

슬픈 영화를 좋아해요?	Do you like sad movies?
저는 슬플 때 슬픈 영화를 보는 걸 좋아해요.	[I like watching sad movies when I'm sad.]
슬픈 영화보다 액션 영화를 더 좋아해요.	[I like action movies more than sad ones.]
슬픈 영화를 볼 때 감정이입을 많이 해요.	[When I watch a sad movie, I empathize a lot.]
코미디나 공포 영화를 더 선호해요.	[I prefer comedies or horror movies more.]
슬픈 영화를 보는 걸 좋아하지 않아요.	[I don't like to watch sad movies.]

Your Turn:

쓰기

영화를 보면 자주 울어요?
[yeong-hwa-reul bo-myeon ja-ju u-reo-yo?]

Try Writing Your Own Answer

1) Write your own answer below to the question -- 영화를 보면 자주 울어요? --

2) Get your answer corrected and rewrite your corrected answer here:

You can post your writing on an app/website like *Hellotalk* or *Hinative* for free corrections.

대화

영화를 보면 자주 울어요?
[yeong-hwa-reul bo-myeon ja-ju u-reo-yo?]

Example Conversation

메리: 마크씨, 영화를 보면서 자주 울어요?
Mark, do you often cry while watching movies?

마크: 아니요. 별로 안 울어요. 하하 메리씨는요?
No, I don't cry much. Haha. What about you, Mary?

메리: 음... 네, 영화가 슬프면 쉽게 우**는 편이에요**.
Um... Yes, if it's a sad movie, I cry pretty easily.

마크: 가장 슬펐던 영화가 뭐였어요?
What's the saddest movie you've seen?

메리: 7번방의 선물이에요. 그 영화를 보면서 펑펑 울었어요.
Miracle in Cell No. 7. I cried my eyes out watching that movie.

마크: 혹시 기생충이라는 영화를 봤어요? 저는 그 영화를 보면서 눈물이 핑 돌았어요.
Have you seen the movie Parasite? I really teared up watching that.

메리: 아, 네! 기생충은 공포영화인데 결말이 슬퍼서 조금 놀랐어요.
Oh, yes! Parasite is a horror movie, so I was a bit surprised the ending was sad.

마크: 네... 사실 저는 아주 슬픈 영화는 잘 안 보**는 편이에요**.
Yeah... Actually I don't tend to watch really sad movies.

메리: 그쵸. 저도 그래요. 마음이 아파서요. 하하
Right? I'm the same way. They break my heart. Haha.

문화

영화를 보면 자주 울어요?
[yeong-hwa-reul bo-myeon ja-ju u-reo-yo?]

Culture Note

기생충

The Korean media and film industry began around 1945, and has grown into a key part of the Korean economy. From 2008 to 2021, the film industry has generated over 1 trillion KRW (over $700m USD) [9].

One of the most famous Korean films in recent times is the movie "Parasite" (기생충). Released in 2019 and directed by Bong Joon-ho (봉준호), "Parasite" was the first non-English language film to win the Academy Award for Best Picture.

Parasite is a black-comedy thriller that follows a poor family, the members of which pose as qualified individuals in order to be hired and invited into the home of a wealthy family. Parasite explores themes like class conflict, social inequality, and wealth disparity. Due to current global similarities across economic, political, and class systems, these particular themes have resonated strongly with international audiences, many of whom have found the plight of the characters tragic and relatable.

202

파티에 가는 것을 좋아하세요?

[pa-ti-e ga-neun geo-seul jo-a-ha-se-yo?]

Do you like to go to parties?

파티 : a party

~에 : location of motion/existence particle

가다 : to go

V~는 것 : verb nominalization; used to change a verb into it's noun form

~을/를 : object particle

좋아하다 : to like

~(으)세요 : honorific present tense sentence ending

대답

파티에 가는 것을 좋아하세요?

[pa-ti-e ga-neun geo-seul jo-a-ha-se-yo?]

Do you like to go to parties?

저는 외향적인 편이에요.

그래서 파티에 자주 가기도 하고 파티를 열기도 해요.

파티에 가면 재미있고 새로운 친구도 사귈 수 있어요!

I'm pretty extroverted.

So I often go to parties, and I host them too.

When you go to parties you can have fun and meet new friends!

Answer Breakdown

Vocabulary	Grammar
Nouns	~은/는 Topic Particle
저 - I; me	~을/를 Object Particle
그래서 - So/Therefore (sentence starter)	A/V~아/어요 Present Tense
파티 - a party	Place~에 가다/오다
자주 - often	N~도
친구 - a friend	그리고, 그래서 & 하지만
Action Verbs	Words of Frequency
가다 - to go	A/V~고, N~(이)고
파티를 열다 - to throw/host/have a party	A/V~(으)면
사귀다 - 1). to make friends; 2). to date	A~ㄴ/은/는 N
Descriptive Verbs	V~(으)ㄹ 수 있다/없다
외향적이다 - to be outgoing; extroverted	A/V~(으)ㄴ/는 편이다
재미있다 - fun; interesting	A/V~기도 하다, N~이기도 하다
새롭다 - to be new	

The grammar is color-coded to match chapters in *Conversational Korean Grammar*.

설명

Grammar Spotlight

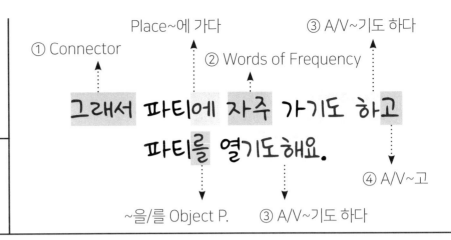

① Connector
Place~에 가다
② Words of Frequency
③ A/V~기도 하다

그래서 파티에 자주 가기도 하고
파티를 열기도해요.

~을/를 Object P.
③ A/V~기도 하다
④ A/V~고

① Sentence Connector 그래서: The word **그래서** (so, therefore) is one of many "sentence connectors." These words always come after a period, beginning a new sentence and linking the two sentences together. **그래서** is used when the preceding sentence is the reason that the next sentence happens.

저는 내성적이에요. **그래서** 파티를 싫어해요.   I'm introverted. So I don't like parties.

지금 살고 있는 아파트는 좁아요. **그래서**   My current apartment is small. So I can't have
파티를 못 열어요.   parties there.

② Words of Frequency 자주: The word **자주** (often) is one of many "frequency words" that are used to talk about how often an action is done or a situation occurs. In the example above, the speaker doesn't just go to/host parties, they **often** go to/host parties.

파티에 가는 걸 좋아해요. 그래서 **자주** 가요.   I like going to parties. So I go often.

시끄러운 음악을 싫어해요. 그래서 파티에   I hate loud music. So I don't go to parties often.
자주 안 가요.

③ A/V~기도 하다: Attach this form to a verb stem when you want to be able to use the **~도** particle - meaning "also/too" - not just with nouns, but with verbs. The verb "가다" (to go) above becomes "가**기도 해요**" (I also go (as well as other actions)).

친구들이랑 자주 외식하**기도 해요**.   I also often go out to eat with my friends.

처음 가는 파티는 어색하**기도 해요**.   Going to a party for the first time is also awkward.

④ A/V~고: The form **~고** is used to connect two clauses in a sentence together with the meaning "and". In the sentence above, clause 1: "파티에 가기도 하다" (I also go to parties) becomes "파티에 가기도 하**고**..." (I also go to parties, and...)

술도 먹**고** 춤도 추기도 해요.   We drink alcohol and we also dance.

친구를 사귀기도 하**고** 게임도 해요.   I also make friends and play games.

문법

A/V~은/는/을 것 같다
[For talking about your thoughts and guesses]

Grammar Practice

A/V~은/는/을 것 같다
Use this form to make guesses. It means "(I) think," or "(something) seems." For the differences between the many possible conjugation rules, check the PDF.

Scan the QR code to view a short grammar lesson PDF.

Given the English sentence below, use the grammar form above to write the equivalent expression in Korean. Including "저는" in your sentences is optional.

1. I think it will rain tomorrow.　　내일 - tomorrow | 비가 오다 - to rain

....

2. It's popular, so I think it'll be delicious.　　인기가 많다 - popular | 맛있다 - delicious

....

3. I think going to parties is fun.　　파티 - party | 가다 - go | 재미있다 - fun

....

4. It seems like it rained outside earlier.　　아까 - earlier | 밖 - outside | 비가 오다 - rain

....

5. I think there will be a party on Friday.　　금요일 - Friday | 있다 - to be/exist

....

ANSWERS: 1. 내일 비가 올 것 같아요. 2. 인기가 많아서 맛있을 것 같아요. 3. 파티에 가는 것 재미있는 것 같아요. 4. 아까 밖에 비가 온 것 같아요. 5. 금요일에 파티가 있을 것 같아요.

Please be aware that not all sentences have one exact translation, so answers may vary slightly.

어휘

파티에 가는 것을 좋아하세요?
[pa-ti-e ga-neun geo-seul jo-a-ha-se-yo?]

Recommended Vocabulary

파티에 가는 것을 좋아하세요? [Do you like going to parties?]

내성적이다 - introverted

외향적이다 - extroverted

아는 사람 - a person I know

모르는 사람 - a person I don't know

답답하다 - to be to be frustrating/suffocating/stuffy

X~에 따라 다르다 - it depends on X

즐기다 - to enjoy

파티를 하다 - to party

파티를 열다 - throw a party

어색하다 - to be awkward

지루하다 - to be bored

놀다 - to play; hang out

어떤 파티에 가요? [What kinds of parties do you go to?]

생일 파티 - a birthday party

송별 파티 - a farewell party

깜짝파티 - a surprise party

크리스마스 파티 - a Christmas party

집들이 - a housewarming party

줄산준비 파티 - a baby shower

신년 파티 - New Years party

파자마 파티 - a pajama party

환영 파티 - a welcome party

졸업식 - a graduation ceremoy

팟럭 피디 - a potluck party

술지리   a drinking party

파티에서 뭘 해요? [What do you do at a party?]

게임을 하다 - to play games

춤을 추다 - to dance

케이크를 먹다 - to eat cake

친구를 사귀다 - to make friends

선물을 교환하다 - to exchange gifts

(음식을) 나눠 먹다 - to share (food)

술게임 - drinking games

얘기하다 - to talk/chat (with)

영화를 보다 - watch a movie

얼마나 자주 파테에 가요? [How often do you go to parties?]

항상 - always

자주 - often

가끔 - sometimes

별로 (+ negative) - not really

절대 (+ negative) - never

주로 - mainly; mostly

보통 - usually; normally

종종 - now and then

전에 - before; in the past

육하원칙

파티에 가는 것을 좋아하세요?
[pa-ti-e ga-neun geo-seul jo-a-ha-se-yo?]

Developing Your Answer

파티에 가는 것을 좋아하세요?	Do you like going to parties?
내성적이라서 파티에 가는 걸 안 좋아해요.	[I'm introverted, so I don't like going to parties.]
외향적이라서 파티에 가는 걸 좋아해요.	[I'm extroverted, so I like going to parties.]
보통 좋아하는데 파티에 따라 달라요.	[I usually like it, but it depends on the party.]
아는 사람이 많은 파티에 가는 걸 좋아해요.	[I like going if there are lots of people I know.]
큰 파티보다 작은 파티를 더 선호해요.	[I prefer small parties to big ones.]

Your Turn:

....

....

어떤 파티에 가요?	What kinds of parties do you go to?
지난 주에 친구의 졸업식 파티에 갔어요.	[I went to my friend's graduation party last week.]
올해 제 생일 파티는 깜짝 파티였어요.	[My birthday party this year was a surprise party.]
매년 회사가 여는 크리스마스 파티에 가요.	[Every year I go to my company's X-mas party.]
이사한 후에 집들이를 했어요.	[I had a housewarming party after I moved.]
최근에 동료를 위해서 송별 파티를 했어요.	[We had a farewell party for my coworker recently.]

Your Turn:

....

....

....

육하원칙

파티에 가는 것을 좋아하세요?
[pa-ti-e ga-neun geo-seul jo-a-ha-se-yo?]

Developing Your Answer

파티에서 뭘 해요?	What do you do at a party?
파자마 파티에서 팝콘을 먹고 영화를 봐요.	[We eat popcorn and watch movies at sleepovers.]
크리스마스 파티에서 선물을 교환했어요.	[We exchanged gifts at the Christmas party.]
신년 파티에서 술게임을 해요.	[We play drinking games at New Year's parties.]
팟럭 파티에서 음식을 나눠 먹었어요.	[We shared food at the potluck.]
파티에서 새로운 친구를 사귀어요.	[I make new friends at parties.]

Your Turn:

얼마나 자주 파티에 가요?	How often do you go to parties?
저는 주말에 종종 파티에 가요.	[I often go to parties on the weekend.]
제 친구 생일에 항상 파티를 열어요.	[I always throw a party on my friend's birthday.]
너무 바빠서 파티는 별로 안 가요.	[I'm too busy, so I rarely go to parties.]
코비드 전에는 많이 갔었어요.	[I went to parties a lot before Covid.]
바쁘지 않으면 가는 편이에요.	[I tend to go when I'm not busy.]

Your Turn:

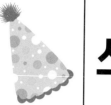

쓰기

파티에 가는 것을 좋아하세요?
[pa-ti-e ga-neun geo-seul jo-a-ha-se-yo?]

Try Writing Your Own Answer

1) Write your own answer below to the question -- 파티에 가는 것을 좋아하세요? --

....
....
....
....
....
....

2) Get your answer corrected and rewrite your corrected answer here:

....
....
....
....
....
....

You can post your writing on an app/website like *Hellotalk* or *Hinative* for free corrections.

대화

파티에 가는 것을 좋아하세요?

[pa-ti-e ga-neun geo-seul jo-a-ha-se-yo?]

Example Conversation

서준: 시우씨, 파티에 가는 것을 좋아하세요?

Shiwoo, do you like going to parties?

시우: 흠... 파티에 따라 달라요. 서준씨는요?

Hm... it depends on the party. How about you, Seojoon?

서준: 저도 **그런 것 같아요**. 지난 주말에 생일카페에 갔는데 정말 좋았어요.

I think I'm the same way. I went to a birthday cafe last weekend, and it was really nice.

시우: 아, 생일카페! 어떤 생일카페에 갔어요?

Oh, a birthday cafe! Which birthday cafe did you go to?

서준: NCT 카페였어요. 태용의 얼굴이 그려진 머그잔을 샀어요. 하하

It was an NCT cafe. I bought a mug with Tae-yong's face on it. Haha.

시우: 그래요? 하하

Really? Haha.

서준: 네, 하하. 시우씨, 생일카페에 가 본 적이 있어요?

Yeah, haha. Have you ever been to a birthday cafe, Shiwoo?

시우: 없지만 우리 언니가 방탄소년단을 좋아해서 콘서트에 같이 많이 가 봤어요.

I haven't, but my older sister likes BTS, so we've gone to lots of concerts together.

서준: 아, 재밌겠다! 정국이의 생일이 얼마 남지 않**은 것 같은**데 생일카페가 있을 거예요.

Oh, sounds fun! I think Jungkook's birthday is coming up, and I bet there'll be a birth-day cafe.

문화

파티에 가는 것을 좋아하세요?
[pa-ti-e ga-neun geo-seul jo-a-ha-se-yo?]

Culture Note

생일카페

A birthday cafe (생일카페) is a fairly recent addition to K-pop culture that has been steadily gaining popularity since 2021. [36]

It is a special fan-held event that takes place at a cafe, in order to celebrate the birthday of a celebrity or idol (a member of a boy group or girl group in K-pop). The idol themselves is not present at the event, but parties like this allow fans to get together and celebrate their favorite idols in their own way.

A large amount of planning goes into arranging a 생일카페. One event held in Seoul to celebrate Mingyu (from the group "Seventeen")'s birthday took three people three months to prepare. Hosts contacted several cafes in order to find a venue, designed cup-sleeves to sell as memorabilia, made posters to hang on the walls, marketed the event on social media, created a raffle with extra prizes and set up a projector to show videos. The event was a great success, with fans lining up on the street in order to visit the event. [24]

개와 고양이 중에 어떤 동물을 좋아해요?

[gae-wa go-yang-i jung-e eo-tteon dong-mu-reul jo-a-hae-yo?]

Do you prefer dogs or cats?

개 : a dog		동물 : an animal	
~와/과 : and (between nouns)		~을/를 : object particle	
고양이 : a cat		좋아하다 : to like	
N 중에(서) : among; out of (all); between		~아/어요 : informal polite present tense	
어떤 : what; what kind of; which			

대답

개와 고양이 중에 어떤 동물을 좋아해요?

[gae-wa go-yang-i jung-e eo-tteon dong-mu-reul jo-a-hae-yo?]

Do you prefer dogs or cats?

고양이를 더 좋아해요.

강아지는 산책도 시키고 옥욕도 시켜야 해서요.

그냥 집 안에서 같이 편하게 쉴 수 있는 고양이를 좋아해요.

I like cats more.
Because you have to walk dogs and give them baths.
I like cats who I can just relax with comfortably inside my house.

Answer Breakdown

Vocabulary	Grammar
Nouns	~을/를 Object Particle
고양이 - a cat	~은/는 Topic Particle
더 - more	Present Tense ~아/어요
강아지 - a dog/puppy	N~도
그냥 - just; only; simply	N~에서
집 - house/home	더 & 덜
안 - in; inside	A/V~고, N~(이)고
같이 - together	A/V~아/어서, N~(이)라서
Action Verbs	V~(으)ㄹ 수 있다/없다
좋아하다 - to like	V~는 N
산책을 시키다 - to walk (sth)	V~아/어야 하다/되다
목욕을 시키다 - to bathe (sth)/give a bath	A~게/이/히
쉬다 - to rest/relax	
Descriptive Verbs	
편하다 - to be comfortable	

The grammar is color-coded to match chapters in *Conversational Korean Grammar*.

설명

Grammar Spotlight

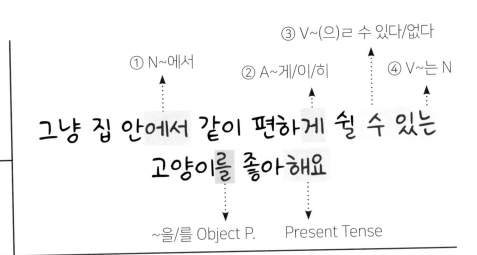

① N~에서

② A~게/이/히

③ V~(으)ㄹ 수 있다/없다

④ V~는 N

그냥 집 안**에서** 같이 편하**게** 쉴 수 있**는** 고양이**를** 좋아**해요**

~을/를 Object P. **Present Tense**

---

① N~에서: This particle attaches to a noun to mark it as the place where some action occurs. The place "집 안" (in/at the house) above is marked by **~에서**, becoming "집 안**에서**" (in/at the house), which is the place where the verb "쉬다" (to rest) happens.

공원**에서** 강아지랑 같이 산책해요.   I walk with my dog at the park.

주말에는 집**에서** 고양이랑 낮잠을 자요.   On the weekend I take naps at home with my cat.

② A~게/이/히: The form **~게/이/히** attaches to descriptive verbs, turning them into adverbs, which are words that can describe HOW a verb happens. Generally these are "-ly" words in English. Attach **~게** to the verb "편하다" (to be comfortable) to make the adverb "편하**게** (comfortably).

공원에서 강아지가 많**이** 놀았어요.   My dog played a lot at the park.

지붕에서 고양이가 천천**히** 걸어 다녀요.   The cat walks slowly on the roof.

③ V~(을) 수 있다/없다: This form attaches to action verb stems, and is used to talk about ability. Attach **~(으)ㄹ 수 있다** to say "I can do..." and **~(으)ㄹ 수 없다** to say "I can't do..." In the example above, the verb "쉬다" (to rest) becomes "**쉴 수 있어요**" (I can rest/relax).

강아지랑 열심히 놀면서 운동 **할 수 있어요**.   You can workout while playing hard with your dog.

고양이에게 캣닙을 많이 주면 취**할수 있어요**.   If you give a cat lots of catnip, they can get high.

④ V~는 N: Use this form to change an action verb into it's present tense noun modifying (adjective) form. Place it in front of a noun to describe that noun as "a **noun** that **verb**s". The verb "쉴 수 있다" (to be able to rest) pairs with "고양이" (cat), becoming "쉴 수 있**는** 고양이" (a cat that can rest).

같이 산책할 수 있**는** 강아지를 좋아해요.   I like dogs that can go for walks with you.

혼자서 놀 수 있**는** 고양이가 좋아요.   I like cats that can play by themselves.

문법

N 중에(서)
[For choosing between or among a group]

Grammar Practice

N 중에(서)
Place this form after a noun when you're choosing one noun from multiple nouns in a group. It means "of all the (nouns)" or "between X and Y." The **(서)** is optional.

Scan the QR code to view a short grammar lesson PDF.

Given the English sentence below, use the grammar form above to write the equivalent expression in Korean. Including "저는" in your sentences is optional.

1. Of all the fruits, I like apples most.

과일 - fruit | 사과 - apple | 좋아하다 - like

2. Between rock and jazz, I like jazz.

재즈 - jazz | 록 - rock

3. Of the exercises, I hate running most.

운동 - exercise | 달리기 - running | 싫다 - hate

4. Tom is the tallest of my friends.

친구들 - friends | 톰 - Tom | 키가 *크다 - tall

5. Chicken is the tastiest of all meats.

고기 - meat | 닭고기 - chicken | 맛있다 - tasty

*Irregular Verb: Be aware that this verb conjugates irregularly.

Please be aware that not all sentences have one exact translation, so answers may vary slightly.

어휘

개와 고양이 중에 어떤 동물을 좋아해요?
[gae-wa go-yang-i jung-e eo-tteon dong-mu-reul jo-a-hae-yo?]

Recommended Vocabulary

개와 고양이 중에 어떤 동물을 좋아해요? [Which animal do you like, dogs or cats?]

좋아하다 - to like

둘 다 - both (of them)

훨씬 더 - a whole lot more

귀엽다 - to be cute

선호하다 - to prefer

고양이 - a cat

조금 더 - a little bit more

애교 - charm/cuteness

싫어하다 - to dislike; to hate

개/강아지 - a dog/puppy

좋다 - to be good; likeable

알레르기가 있다 - allergic to

개나 고양이를 키우나요? [Do you have a dog or cat?]

(애완동물)을 키우다 - to have/keep/raise (a pet)

애완동물 - pets

졸다 - to doze

매력적이다 - charming/at-tractive

우리 집 - my house/family

먹이를 주다 - to feed

(강아지) 두 마리 - two (dogs)
(고양이) 한 마리 - one (cat)

털 - fur

고양이 카페 - a cat cafe

개의 어떤 점을 좋아해요? [What do you like about dogs?]

짖다 - to bark

활발하다 - to be active/energetic

반갑다 - to greet

뛰어오르다 - to run/jump up

뛰어놀다 - to romp/frolic

친근하다 - to be friendly

물어뜯다 - to chew/gnaw on

충성심이 좋다 - to be loyal

꼬리를 흔들다 - to wag a tail

산책시키다 - to walk (a pet)

옆에 붙이다 - to stick next to

핥다 - to lick

고양이의 어떤 점을 좋아해요? [What do you like about cats?]

쓰다듬다 - to pet/pat

숨다 - to hide

순하다 - to be gentle

장난기가 많다 - to be playful

조용하다 - to be quiet

까탈스럽다 - to be fussy

차분하다 - to be calm

고양이 장난감 - a cat toy

쉬다 - to rest/relax

독립적이다 - independent

깔끔하다 - to be neat/clean

우아하다 - to be graceful

육하원칙

개와 고양이 중에 어떤 동물을 좋아해요?
[gae-wa go-yang-i jung-e eo-tteon dong-mu-reul jo-a-hae-yo?]

Developing Your Answer

개와 고양이 중에 어떤 동물을 좋아해요?	Which animal do you like, dogs or cats?
저는 강아지를 더 좋아해요.	[I like dogs more.]
저는 고양이를 더 좋아해요.	[I like cats more.]
둘 다 좋은데 고양이를 조금 더 좋아해요.	[They're both great, but I like cats a little bit more.]
고양이를 좋아하는데 알레르기가 있어요.	[I like cats, but I'm allergic to them.]
강아지는 애교가 더 많아서 좋아해요.	[I like dogs because they act cuter.]

Your Turn:

....

....

....

개나 고양이를 키우나요?	Do you have a dog or cat?
지금은 애완동물을 안 키우고 있어요.	[I don't have a pet right now.]
우리 집은 고양이 세 마리를 키워요.	[My family has three cats.]
우리 집에는 귀여운 강아지가 있어요.	[I have a cute dog at home.]
고양이 알레르기가 있어서 못 키워요.	[I'm allergic to cats, so I can't have one.]
우리 아파트는 애완견 금지예요.	[Our apartment doesn't allow pets.]

Your Turn:

....

....

....

육하원칙

개와 고양이 중에 어떤 동물을 좋아해요?
[gae-wa go-yang-i jung-e eo-tteon dong-mu-reul jo-a-hae-yo?]

Developing Your Answer

개의 어떤 점을 좋아해요?	What do you like about dogs?
강아지를 산책시키는 걸 좋아해요.	[I like walking my dog.]
강아지는 귀엽고 저를 행복하게 만들어요.	[Dogs are cute, and they make me happy.]
개들은 친근하고 활발한 동물이에요.	[Dogs are friendly, active animals.]
우리 강아지는 항상 저를 반가워해요.	[My dog always greets me.]
개들은 충성심이 좋아요.	[Dogs are loyal.]

Your Turn:

고양이의 어떤 점을 좋아해요?	What do you like about cats?
고양이는 보통 우아하고 차분해요.	[Cats are generally graceful and calm.]
우리 집에 있는 고양이는 귀여워요.	[The cat I have at home is cute.]
고양이는 산책시키지 않아도 돼서 좋아요.	[I like that you don't have to walk cats.]
제 고양이는 까탈스럽지만 깔끔해요.	[My cat is fussy, but clean.]
고양이는 독립적이지만 쓰다듬는 걸 좋아헤요.	[My cat is independent, but loves getting petted.]

Your Turn:

쓰기

개와 고양이 중에 어떤 동물을 좋아해요?
[gae-wa go-yang-i jung-e eo-tteon dong-mu-reul jo-a-hae-yo?]

Try Writing Your Own Answer

1) Write your own answer below to the question   -- 개와 고양이 중에 어떤 동물을 좋아해요? --

2) Get your answer corrected and rewrite your corrected answer here:

You can post your writing on an app/website like *Hellotalk* or *Hinative* for free corrections.

대화

개와 고양이 중에 어떤 동물을 좋아해요?
[gae-wa go-yang-i jung-e eo-tteon dong-mu-reul jo-a-hae-yo?]

Example Conversation

이준: 강아지와 고양이 **중에** 어떤 동물을 좋아하세요?
  Do you prefer dogs or cats?

은우: 저는... 고양이가 조용하고 순해서 고양이를 조금 더 좋아해요. 개는 좀 무서워요.
  For me... cats are quiet and gentle, so I like cats a bit more. Dogs are a little scary.

이준: 아, 그래요? 우리 집 강아지는 아주 귀여운데... 강아지를 왜 무서워하게 됐어요?
  Oh, really? But my dog is so cute... how did you end up scared of dogs?

은우: 저는 어렸을 때 시골에서 살았어요. 학교 가는 길에 항상 으르렁거리는 개들이 자주 쫓아왔었어요.
  When I was young I lived in the countryside, and growling dogs always chased me on my way to school.

이준: 아, 네. 정말 무서웠겠네요.
  Oh my. That must have been really scary.

은우: 네, 맞아요. 지금은 사람들이 개를 집에서 안전하게 키우는 걸 알지만 저는 아직도 개를 만나면 무서워요.
  Yes, it was. I know people raise dogs safely at home nowadays, but if I meet a dog I'm still scared.

이준: 네, 이해해요. 걱정마세요. 더 순한 강아지를 만나면 좀 더 편안해질 것 같아요.
  Yes, I get it. Don't worry. You might get more comfortable with them if you meet some gentler dogs.

문화

개와 고양이 중에 어떤 동물을 좋아해요?
[gae-wa go-yang-i jung-e eo-tteon dong-mu-reul jo-a-hae-yo?]

Culture Note

개

Dogs have a long history in Korea, and the Korean peninsula has a variety of dog breeds native to the area, the most famous being the Jindo dog (진돗개). South Koreans, however, historically regarded dogs as edible farm animals, not loving indoor companions. [25]

Dog meat is still available in Korea, although it is becoming increasingly unpopular as more and more people begin raising dogs as members of the family. These days about 70 percent of South Korea's population disapprove of eating dog, and 48% of Korean people said they have never eaten dog meat. For the minority of people who do still eat dog, the meat is most often consumed on boknal (복날 - the three hottest days on the lunar calendar) due to the cultural belief that eating it helps the body cope with heat and humidity. [25]

Currently, dog meat is neither legal nor explicitly banned in South Korea. But in November of 2021, the South Korean government announced they are considering outlawing dog meat consumption. [26]

Q22

싫어하는 음식은 뭐예요?

[si-reo-ha-neun eum-si-geun mwo-e-yo?]

What foods do you hate?

싫어하다 : to dislike; to hate
V~는 N : present tense noun-modifying (adjective) form
음식 : food
~은/는 : topic particle
뭐 : what
~이에요/예요 : the copula "to be"

대답

싫어하는 음식은 뭐예요?
[si-reo-ha-neun eum-si-geun mwo-e-yo?]
What foods do you hate?

고수를 싫어해요.
근데 엄마는 고수를 좋아해서 고수가 들어간 음식을 요리해요.
저는 그때마다 고수를 빼야 해서 짜증나요.

I hate cilantro,
But my mom likes cilantro, so she cooks food with cilantro in it.
Every time she does it I have to pick out the cilantro, so it's annoying.

Answer Breakdown

Vocabulary	Grammar
Nouns	~을/를 Object Particle
고수 - cilantro; coriander	~은/는 Topic Particle
근데 - But/However (sentence starter)	~이/가 Subject Particle
엄마 - (my) mom	Present Tense ~아/어요
음식 - food	A/V~아/어서, N~(이)라서
저 - I; me	A~ㄴ/은/는 N
그때 - that time; those times; then	A/V~ㄹ/을 때, N 때
Action Verbs	N~마다
싫어하다 - to dislike; to hate	V~아/어야 하다/되다
좋아하다 - to like	
요리하다 - to cook	
빼다 - to remove; to take sth out	
Descriptive Verbs	
들어가다 - 1). to contain; 2). to go in	
짜증나다 - to be annoying	

The grammar is color-coded to match chapters in *Conversational Korean Grammar*.

설명

Grammar Spotlight

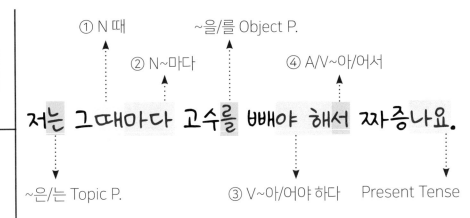

① N 때

② N~마다

~을/를 Object P.

④ A/V~아/어서

저는 그때마다 고수를 빼야 해서 짜증나요.

~은/는 Topic P.

③ V~아/어야 하다

Present Tense

① **A/V~ㄹ/을 때, N 때:** Although we have highlighted this grammar form as being "**N 때**," the word "그때" (that time/those times/then) should be written as one word (i.e. with no space between "그" and "때"). The grammar form "**N 때**" is related, but not exactly the same thing.

매운 음식을 먹**을 때** 혀가 아파요.   My tongue hurts when I eat spicy food.

버섯을 먹**을 때** 속이 울렁거려요.   When I eat mushrooms I feel nauseous.

② **N~마다:** This form means "each/every/all," and it can be attached to a noun to say "every N." When attached to time nouns it indicates that some action or situation repeats over a period of time. In the sentence above, **~마다** attaches to the noun "그때"(that time/those times/then), ultimately creating "그때**마다**" (every time/at those times).

콩밥을 먹을 때**마다** 콩을 빼요.   Whenever I eat kongbap, I take out the beans.

두리안 냄새를 맡을 때**마다** 토할 것 같아요.   Whenever I smell durian I feel like throwing up.

③ **V~아/어야 하다:** This form is used to say that you "have to" "must" or "should" do a verb. In the example above, the verb "빼다" (to take out/remove) becomes "빼**야 해요**" (I have to/must/should remove it).

매일 밥을 먹을 때마다 김치를 먹**어야 해요**.   Everyday when I eat, I have to have kimchi.

피자를 먹을 때마다 올리브를 빼**야 해요**.   Whenever I eat pizza I have to take off the olives.

④ **A/V~아/어서:** The form **~아/어서** attaches to the verb stem to connect two clauses. It is used when clause 1 of a sentence is the reason that clause 2 happens, and it means "so/since/because." In the example above, clause 1: "... 고수를 빼야 하다" (... I have to remove the cilantro), becomes "... 고수를 빼야 **해서**..." (... I have to remove the cilantro, so...)

점심을 짜게 먹**어서** 물을 많이 마셔야 해요.   Lunch was salty, so I have to drink a lot of water.

굴이 신선하지 않**아서** 뱉어야 했어요.   The oysters weren't fresh, so I had to spit them out.

문법

A/V~아/어도
[To connect clauses with "even if"]

Grammar Practice

A/V~아/어도
Connect two clauses in a sentence with the meaning "even if." Attach **~아/어도** to the final verb in the first clause. Show overall tense on the final verb in clause two.

Scan the QR code to view a short grammar lesson PDF.

Given the English sentence below, use the grammar form above to write the equivalent expression in Korean. Including "저는" in your sentences is optional.

1. Even if fried chicken is tasty, I don't eat it often.   치킨 - fried chicken | 맛있다 - tasty

....

2. Even if I workout hard, I don't lose weight.   열심히 - hard | 살이 빠지다 - lose weight

....

3. Even if a food is unfamiliar, I can eat it well.   음식 - food | 낯설다 - unfamiliar

....

4. Even if it's cold, I drink iced coffee.   *춥다 - cold | 아이스 커피 - iced coffee

....

5. Even if I sleep in, I'm always tired.   늦잠을 자다 - to sleep in | 피곤하다 - tired

....

*Irregular Verb: Be aware that this verb conjugates irregularly.

Please be aware that not all sentences have one exact translation, so answers may vary slightly.

어휘

싫어하는 음식은 뭐예요?
[si-reo-ha-neun eum-si-geun mwo-e-yo?]

Recommended Vocabulary

싫어하는 음식은 뭐예요? [What food(s) do you hate?]

올리브 - olives	오이 - cucumbers	토마토 - tomatoes
고수 - cilantro/coriander	블루 치즈 - blue cheese	버섯 - mushrooms
비트 - beets	멸치 - anchovies	브로콜리 - broccoli
코티지 치즈 - cottage cheese	굴 - oysters	아보카도 - avocado
가지 - eggplant	두리안 - durian	두부 - tofu

그 음식을 왜 싫어해요? [Why do you hate it?]

느끼하다 - to be greasy	식감 - a food texture	맛 - a taste
냄새 - a smell	최악 - the worst	맵다 - to be spicy
물컹하다 - to be squishy	고약하다 - disgusting (smell)	냄새가 나다 - to smell/stink
맛없다 - to taste bad	물렁물렁하다 - to be mushy	비린내 - a fishy smell
특유의 (X) - particular (X)	쓰다 - to be bitter	참다 - to tolerate/handle

언제부터 이 음식을 싫어했어요? [Since when have you hated this food?]

원래 - originally/always	처음부터 - from the start	요새 - lately
항상 - always	오랫동안 - for a long time	몇 년 - a few years

싫어하는 음식을 먹으면 어떤 기분이에요? [How do you feel when you eat it?]

토하다 - to throw up	속이 뒤틀리다 - one's stomach turns/churns	속이 거북하다 - to be bloated
견디다 - to tolerate		혀가 아프다 - tongue hurts
비누 맛 - a soapy taste	나쁘다 - to be bad	뱉다 - to spit out
속이 울렁거리다 - nauseous	편식하다 - to be picky	속 쓰리다 - to get heartburn

싫어하는 음식은 뭐예요?
[si-reo-ha-neun eum-si-geun mwo-e-yo?]

Developing Your Answer

싫어하는 음식은 뭐예요?	What food(s) do you hate?
저는 멸치를 싫어해요.	[I hate anchovies.]
제가 가장 싫어하는 음식은 블루 치즈예요.	[The food I hate the most is blue cheese.]
굴은 그냥 싫어하지만 비트는 최악이에요.	[I don't like oysters, but beets are the worst.]
두부는 징그러워서 먹지 않아요.	[Tofu is gross, so I don't eat it.]
저는 항상 토마토를 싫어했어요.	[I've always hated tomatoes.]

Your Turn:

그 음식을 왜 싫어해요?	Why do you hate it?
가지의 물렁물렁한 식감을 못 참겠어요.	[I can't handle the mushy texture of eggplant.]
블루 치즈는 아주 쓴 맛이 있기 때문이에요.	[Because blue cheese has a really bitter taste.]
두리안의 특유의 고약한 냄새가 싫어요.	[I hate that particularly terrible smell durian has.]
오이 특유의 비린내가 있어서 못 먹어요.	[Cucumbers have a fishy smell, so I can't eat them.]
버섯의 물컹한 식감을 좋아하지 않아요.	[I don't like the squishy texture of mushrooms.]

Your Turn:

육하원칙

싫어하는 음식은 뭐예요?
[si-reo-ha-neun eum-si-geun mwo-e-yo?]

Developing Your Answer

언제부터 이 음식을 싫어했어요?	Since when have you hated this food?
어렸을 때부터 브로콜리를 싫어했어요.	[I've hated broccoli ever since I was young.]
처음부터 고수는 제 취향이 아닌 것 같아요.	[I think cilantro has never been my thing.]
원래 괜찮았는데 요새 가지가 싫어졌어요.	[I was ok with it before, but lately I hate eggplant.]
식중독에 걸린 이후로 생선을 안 먹고 있어요.	[After the food poisoning I don't eat fish anymore.]
채식주의자가 된 이후로 고기는 안 먹어요.	[Since becoming a vegetarian I don't eat meat.]

Your Turn:

싫어하는 음식을 먹으면 어떤 기분이에요?	How do you feel when you eat it?
토마토를 먹으면 토할 것 같아요.	[I feel like throwing up if I eat tomatoes.]
고수를 먹으면 비누 맛이 나요.	[When I eat cilantro, it tastes like soap.]
제 혀에 닿으면 즉시 뱉어요.	[If it touches my tongue I immediately spit it out.]
고추는 매워서 먹으면 혀가 아파요.	[Peppers are spicy, so if I eat them my tongue hurts.]
비트를 먹을 생각만 해도 속이 메스꺼워요.	[Just the thought of eating beets makes me sick.]

Your Turn:

쓰기

싫어하는 음식은 뭐예요?
[si-reo-ha-neun eum-si-geun mwo-e-yo?]

Try Writing Your Own Answer

1) Write your own answer below to the question   --   싫어하는 음식은 뭐예요?   --

2) Get your answer corrected and rewrite your corrected answer here:

You can post your writing on an app/website like *Hellotalk* or *Hinative* for free corrections.

대화

싫어하는 음식은 뭐예요?
[si-reo-ha-neun eum-si-geun mwo-e-yo?]

Example Conversation

민준: 제인씨, 싫어하는 음식이 있어요?
Jane, are there any foods you don't like?

제인: 저는 입맛이 까다롭지 않아서 왠만한 건 거의 다 먹어요. 민준씨는요?
I'm not picky, so I'll eat almost anything. How about you, Minjoon?

민준: 저는 좀 까다로운 편이긴 **해도** 한번은 먹으려고 시도는 해요. 오이는 빼고요.
I'm a bit picky, but I'll try anything once. Except for cucumbers.

제인: 정말요? 오이를 싫어하세요?
Really? Do you hate cucumbers?

민준: 네, 오이의 비린내를 싫어하기 때문이에요.
Yes, because I hate that fishy smell cucumbers have.

제인: 비린내? 저는 오이를 **아무리** 많이 **먹어도** 비린맛을 느껴 본 적이 없어요.
Fishy smell? No matter how many cucumbers I have, I've never tasted anything fishy.

민준: 진짜 비린 맛이 아니고 그냥 오이의 특별한 맛을 좋아하지 않아요.
It's not really a fishy taste, I just don't like that particular taste cucumbers have.

제인: 아, 그렇구나. 저는 오이의 비린 맛이 있다는 걸 처음 알았어요. 하하
Ah, okay. This is the first time I'm hearing that cucumbers have a fishy taste. Haha.

문화

싫어하는 음식은 뭐예요?
[si-reo-ha-neun eum-si-geun mwo-e-yo?]

Culture Note

오이의 비린내

Cucumber haters are prevalent in Korea, with many people claiming to despise their texture, taste, and even smell. [27]

Cucumber haters complain about the "fishy smell" (비린내) of cucumbers. The smell is not actually fishy though, so 비린내 is merely an exaggeration adopted to describe the bitter scent cucumbers have for some people. There might even be a medical basis for it, with a certain gene leading cucumbers to taste and smell terrible for some people [28].

In Korea, a Facebook Group called "Cucumber Haters Unite" (오이를 싫어하는 사람들의 모임) has over 90,000 likes, with numerous people coming together to share their hatred of this particular fruit. [29]

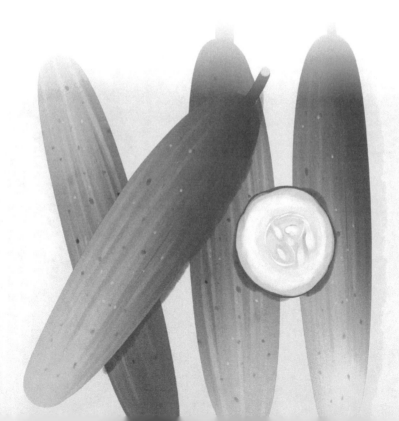

Q23

혼자서 살고 싶어요?

[hon-ja-seo sal-go si-peo-yo?]

Do you want to live alone?

혼자(서) : alone; on one's own; by oneself

살다 : to live

V~고 싶다 : to want to do some verb

~아/어요 : informal polite present tense

대답

혼자서 살고 싶어요?
[hon-ja-seo sal-go si-peo-yo?]
Do you want to live alone?

혼자서 살아 보고 싶어요.
하지만 요즘 집값이 비싸져서 살 여유가 없을 것 같아요.
어쩔 수 없이 다른 사람과 같이 살아야 될 것 같아요!

I want to try living alone.
But these days houses are getting expensive, so I don't think I'll be able to afford to buy one.
I feel like I have no choice but to live with someone else!

Answer Breakdown

Vocabulary	Grammar
Nouns	~이/가 Subject Particle
혼자(서) - alone; by oneself	Present Tense ~아/어요
하지만 - But/However (sentence starter)	V~고 싶다
요즘 - these days; recently; nowadays; lately	그리고, 그래서 & 하지만
집값 - house prices; housing prices	A/V~아/어서, N~(이)라서
여유 - affordability; availability	A~ㄴ/은/는 N
사람 - person	N~와/과, N~(이)랑, N~하고
같이 - together	V~아/어 보다
Action Verbs	V~(으)ㄹ N
살다 - to live	A~아/어지다
사다 - to buy	A/V~은/는/을 것 같다
Descriptive Verbs	A~게/이/히
비싸다 - to be expensive	V~아/어야 하다/되다
없다 - to not exist; to not have	
어쩔 수 없다 - to be inevitable; have no choice	
다르다 - to be different	

The grammar is color-coded to match chapters in *Conversational Korean Grammar*.

설명

Grammar Spotlight

③ V~(으)ㄹ N

① A~아/어지다

④ A/V~은/는/을 것 같다

집값이 비싸져서 살 여유가 없을 것 같아요.

② A/V~아/어서

Present Tense

~이/가 Subject P.

~이/가 Subject P.

① A~아/어지다: When attached to a descriptive verb, this form allows you to talks about a change in state over time. In English we think of this as "more adjective" or "adjective-er" The verb "비싸다" (to be expensive) becomes "비**싸져요**" (it gets/becomes more expensive).

작년보다 집값이 **싸졌어요**.   The housing prices are cheaper than last year.

동네가 시끄러**워졌어요**.   My neighborhood has gotten noisier.

② A/V~아/어서: The form **~아/어서** attaches to the verb stem to connect two clauses. It is used when clause 1 of a sentence is the reason that clause 2 happens, and it means "so/since/because." In the above sentence, clause 1: "집값이 비싸지다" (houses are getting expensive), becomes "집값이 비싸**져서**..." (because/since houses are getting expensive...").

월세가 비싸**져서** 룸메이트와 살아요.   I live with a roommate because my rent went up.

자취를 시작**해서** 행복해졌어요.   I've been happier since I moved out.

③ V~(으)ㄹ N: This is a noun modifying (adjective) form for future tense actions, with the meaning of "a noun that will be acted on." The verb "사다" (to buy) above modifies "여유가 없다" (to be able to afford), becoming "**살** 여유가 없어요" (I won't be able to afford to buy it).

이사**할** 여유가 없어서 재계약했어요.   I can't afford to move, so I renewed my lease.

새로 **살** 집에 수영장이 있어서 좋아요.   It's nice that the house I'm buying has a pool.

④ A/V~은/는/을 것 같아요: This form is used to express a guess or supposition. It can attach to any verb, and means "it seems like" or "I think that." In the example above "여유가 없다" becomes "여유가 없**을 것 같아요**." (I don't think I'll be able to afford to buy it).

내년엔 혼자 살 집을 구할 수 있**을 것 같아요**.   I think I'll be able to get a place to myself next year.

함께 살 친구와 친해서 괜찮**을 것 같아요**.   I'm close with the friend I'm going to live with, so I think it'll be fine.

문법

A~아/어지다
[To talk about things changing]

Grammar Practice

A~아/어지다

This form allows you to say that a subject is "getting/becoming more (adjective)." It indicates a change in state over time.

Scan the QR code to view a short grammar lesson PDF.

Given the English sentence below, use the grammar form above to write the equivalent expression in Korean. Including "저는" in your sentences is optional.

1. I want to be healthier, so I eat veggies.　　건강하다 - healthy | 야채 - veggies | 먹다 - eat

....

2. Lately the weather has gotten cooler.　　요즘 - lately | 날씨 - weather | 시원하다 - cool

....

3. I caught a cold, but I've gotten better.　　감기 - a cold | 걸리다 - catch | *낫다 - better

....

4. The rent has gotten more expensive.　　집세 - rent | 비싸다 - expensive

....

5. If I want to be smarter, I have to study.　　똑똑하다 - smart | 공부하다 - study

....

*Irregular Verb: Be aware that this verb conjugates irregularly.

ANSWERS: 1. 건강해지고 싶어서 야채를 먹어요. 2. 요즘 날씨가 시원해졌어요. 3. 감기에 걸렸지만 나아졌어요. 4. 집세가 비싸졌어요. 5. 똑똑해지고 싶으면 공부해야 해요.

Please be aware that not all sentences have one exact translation, so answers may vary slightly.

어휘

혼자서 살고 싶어요?
[hon-ja-seo sal-go si-peo-yo?]

Recommended Vocabulary

혼자서 살고 싶어요? [Do you want to live alone?]

살다 - to live

같이/함께 - together

가족 - family

다른 사람 - another person; someone else

잘 아는 사람 - a person I know well

잘 모르는 사람 - a person I don't know well

지금 누구랑 살고 있나요? [Are you living with someone right now?]

룸메이트 - a roommate

아파트 - apartment

집 - house/home

친척 - a relative

부모님 - parents

현제 - siblings

남편 - husband

아내 - wife

사다 - to buy

친구 - a friend

강아지 - a dog/puppy

고양이 - a cat

애인 - a partner; a lover

여자친구 - a girlfriend

남자친구 - a boyfriend

얼마나 지금 살고 있는 곳에 살았어요? [How long have you lived at your current place?]

태어나다 - to be born

집을 얻다 - to get a house

결혼하다 - to get married

5년 동안 - for 5 years

졸업하다 - to graduate

몇 년 - a few years

작년 - last year

내년 - next year

이사하다 - to move (houses)

왜 혼자/같이 살고 싶어요? [Why do you want to live alone/with someone?]

비싸다 - to be expensive

싸다 - to be cheap

돈을 모으다 - to save money

가능하다 - possible

불가능하다 - impossible

시끄럽다 - to be loud/noisy

외롭다 - to be lonely

행복하다 - to be happy

짜증나다 - to be annoying

재미있다 - fun; interesting

안전하다 - to be safe

위험하다 - to be dangerous

집세 - rent (payment)

필요하다 - to need

집값 - house price

심심하다 - to be bored

(집)을 빌리다 - to rent a (house)

개인적인 공간 - personal space

237

육하원칙

혼자서 살고 싶어요?
[hon-ja-seo sal-go si-peo-yo?]

Developing Your Answer

혼자서 살고 싶어요?	Do you want to live alone?
아니요 혼자서 살면 외로울 것 같아요.	[No, I think I'll be lonely if I live alone.]
네, 다른 사람이랑 살고 싶지 않아요.	[Yes, I don't want to live with someone else.]
혼자 살면 가족이 보고 싶을 거예요.	[I'll miss my family if I live by myself.]
친구랑 살아 보고 싶어요.	[I want to try living with my friend.]
잘 모르는 사람과 함께 살 수 없어요.	[I can't live with someone I don't know well.]

Your Turn:

....

....

....

지금 누구랑 살고 있나요?	Are you living with someone right now?
지금 룸메이트랑 같이 아파트에 살아요.	[I'm living with a roommate in an apartment.]
혼자서 아파트에서 살고 있어요.	[I'm living in an apartment alone.]
결혼해서 아내와 살고 있어요.	[I'm married, so I'm living with my wife.]
아기 고양이와 함께 살고 있어요.	[I'm living with a kitten.]
남자친구와 같이 월세로 살고 있어요.	[I'm renting a place with my boyfriend.]

Your Turn:

....

....

....

238

육하원칙

혼자서 살고 싶어요?
[hon-ja-seo sal-go si-peo-yo?]

Developing Your Answer

얼마나 지금 살고 있는 곳에 살았어요?	How long have you lived at your current place?
태어났을 때부터 부모님과 함께 살았어요.	[I've lived with my parents since I was born.]
작년에 제 룸메이트랑 여기로 이사했어요.	[I moved here with my roommate last year.]
졸업한 다음에 이 아파트로 이사했어요.	[I moved to this apartment after I graduated.]
결혼한 후에 아내랑 이 집을 얻었어요.	[My wife and I got this house after our wedding.]
여기에 10년 정도 살았지만 이사하고 싶어요.	[I've been here about 10 years, but I want to move.]

Your Turn:

왜 혼자/같이 살고 싶어요?	Why do you want to live alone/with someone?
나만의 개인적인 공간이 필요해요.	[I need my own personal space.]
누구랑 같이 살면 돈을 모을 수 있어요.	[I can save money if I live with someone.]
친구랑 같이 살면 매일 재미있을 것 같아요.	[Every day would be fun living with my friends.]
다른 사람이랑 사는 건 시끄럽고 짜증나요.	[Living with other people is noisy and annoying.]
나만 있으면 심심할 것 같아요.	[I think it'd be boring if it was just me.]

Your Turn:

239

쓰기

혼자서 살고 싶어요?
[hon-ja-seo sal-go si-peo-yo?]

Try Writing Your Own Answer

1) Write your own answer below to the question -- 혼자서 살고 싶어요? --

2) Get your answer corrected and rewrite your corrected answer here:

You can post your writing on an app/website like *Hellotalk* or *Hinative* for free corrections.

대화

혼자서 살고 싶어요?
[hon-ja-seo sal-go si-peo-yo?]

Example Conversation

케빈: 대니씨, 다른 사람과 같이 살고 싶어요? 아니면 혼자서 살고 싶어요?
Danny, do you want to live with another person? Or do you want to live alone?

대니: 저는 혼자서 살 수 있었으면 좋겠어요. 하지만 그러면 돈이 너무 많이 들어요.
I wish I could live alone. But if I did it would cost too much.

케빈: 맞아요. 물가도 너무 올랐고 집값도 정말 비싸**졌어요**.
Right. The cost of living went up a lot, and house prices have gotten really expensive.

대니: 네. 지금은 대학교에 다니고 있어서 그냥 부모님과 함께 사는데, 그게 많이 절약할 수 있어요.
Yes. Since I'm going to college now, I'm living with my parents, so I can save a lot.

케빈: 졸업 후에는 어떻게 할 생각이에요?
What do you think you'll do after graduation?

대니: 좋은 직업을 가진다면 자취할 수 있겠지만... 아직은 확실하지 않아요.
If I get a good job, I'd be able to leave home, but... I'm still not really sure yet.

케빈: 그쵸, 그래서 저는 룸메이트랑 같이 살고 있어요. 더 싸니까요.
Right, that's why I'm living with a roommate. Since it's cheaper.

대니: 맞아요, 누군가와 같이 살면 돈을 설약할 수 있을 것 같아요. 저도 나중에 자취를 하면 룸메이트와 사는 것을 고려해 볼게요.
Definitely, I think you can really save money by living with someone else. If I move out later I'll consider getting a roommate.

문화

혼자서 살고 싶어요?
[hon-ja-seo sal-go si-peo-yo?]

Culture Note

자취

자취 literally means 'cooks by oneself,' which is a term used for the lifestyle of living alone in Korea. However, it's not an attainable lifestyle for many young Koreans nowadays. In a 2021 report by Statistics Korea, less than 40% of unmarried people aged between 20 and 44 have moved out of home.

Korean youth face high unemployment and high housing prices. In 2017, only 42% of youth aged 15-29 were employed, compared to the OECD average of 53%. [37] From May 2017 to November 2021, apartment prices in Seoul have increased 109% - the cost reaching ₩1.29 billion KRW (almost $1 million USD) to purchase a 1,000 square foot (100 square meter) apartment. This has increased the time it takes for the average Seoul worker to buy an apartment from income savings from 20 years to 38 years. [38]

As a result, many young Korean adults are choosing not to leave the nest. However, cultural differences also play a part, as Korea is a more collectivist society with family groups tending to live together longer. There is also less of a stigma about living at home, especially as people realize the difficulty of achieving financial independence. In addition, many Korean parents are quite happy to keep their children at home so that the family members can provide mutual companionship and care. [31]

아침형 인간이에요?
저녁형 인간이에요?

[a-chim-hyeong in-ga-ni-e-yo? cheo-nyeok-hyeong in-ga-ni-e-yo?]

Are you a morning person, or a night owl?

아침형 : morning type; an "early bird"	
인간 : human; person	
저녁형 : evening/night type; a "night owl"	
~이에요/예요 : the copula "to be"	

대답

아침형 인간이에요? 저녁형 인간이에요?

[a-chim-hyeong in-ga-ni-e-yo? cheo-nyeok-hyeong in-ga-ni-e-yo?]

Are you a morning person, or a night owl?

저는 아침형 인간이 아니에요.

하지만 평소에는 직장 때문에 일찍 일어나야 해요.

하지만 주말에는 밤늦게 자고 아침에 늦게 일어나요.

I'm not a morning person.
But I usually have to get up early because of work.
However, on weekends I go to bed late at night, and get up late in the morning.

Answer Breakdown

Vocabulary	Grammar
Nouns	~은/는 Topic Particle
저 - I; me	N~(이/가) 아니에요
아침형 인간 - a morning person	Present Tense ~아/어요
하지만 - But/However (sentence starter)	Time~에 V
평소에 - ordinarily; usually; normally	그리고, 그래서 & 하지만
직장 - work; one's workplace	보통, 주로 & 평소에
일찍 - early	A/V~고, N~(이)고
주말 - weekend	N 때문에
아침 - morning; breakfast	V~아/어야 하다/되다
Action Verbs	A~게/이/히
일어나다 - to wake up; to get up	
자다 - to sleep; to go to bed	
Descriptive Verbs	
밤늦다 - to be late at night	
늦다 - to be late	

The grammar is color-coded to match chapters in Conversational Korean Grammar.

설명

Grammar Spotlight

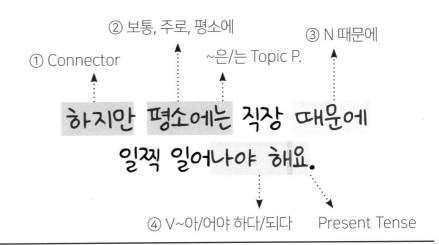

① Connector

② 보통, 주로, 평소에

~은/는 Topic P.

③ N 때문에

하지만 평소에는 직장 때문에 일찍 일어나야 해요.

④ V~아/어야 하다/되다

Present Tense

① **Sentence Connector 하지만:** The word **하지만** (but, however) is one of many "sentence connectors." These words always come after a period, beginning a new sentence and linking the two sentences together. **하지만** is used when two sentences are being contrasted.

저는 아침형 인간이에요. **하지만** 남편은 저녁형 인간이에요.	I'm a morning person. But my husband is an evening person.
저녁에 집중력이 좋아서 일이 잘 돼요. **하지만** 아침에 일어나기 힘들어요.	I work well at night because I can concentrate well. But getting up in the morning is hard.

② **보통, 주로 & 평소에:** These are all words that can be placed in a sentence to mean "usually." They are highly interchangeable, but "평소에" includes the meaning of "on a regular day."

보통 일찍 일어나요. 하지만 주말은 늦잠자요.	I usually get up early. But I sleep in on the weekend.
주로 아침에 커피를 마셔요. 하지만 저녁에는 따뜻한 물을 마셔요.	I mainly have coffee in the morning. But in the evening I drink warm water.

③ **N 때문에:** When following a noun, this form can be used to give a reason, meaning something like "because of noun" in English. In the example above, it follows the noun "직장" (work/workplace), making "직장 **때문에**" (because of work/because of my workplace...).

아이들 **때문에** 보통 일찍 일어나요.	I usually get up early because of my kids.
늦게 자는 습관 **때문에** 보통 아침에 피곤해요.	I'm usually tired in the morning because I go to bed late.

④ **V~아/어야 하다:** This form is used to say that you "have to" "must" or "should" do a verb. In the example above, the verb "일어나다" (to wake up; to get up) becomes "일어나**야 해요**" (I have to/must/should wake up).

일 때문에 일찍 **자야 해요**.	I have to go to bed early because of work.
기말고사 때문에 밤 늦게까지 공부**해야 해요**.	I have finals, so I have to study until late at night.

245

문법

V~아/어야 하다
[For talking about things you should do/have to do]

Grammar Practice

V~아/어야 하다
This form adds the meaning of "should/have to/must" to your sentence. You can also use the form **~아/어야 되다**, though it is slightly more casual.

Scan the QR code to view a short grammar lesson PDF.

Given the English sentence below, use the grammar form above to write the equivalent expression in Korean. Including "저는" in your sentences is optional.

1. I have to do well on my final exam.
기말고사 - final exam | 보다 - take a test

....

2. If you have time, you should rest.
시간 - time | 있다 - have | 쉬다 - rest

....

3. I want to go home, but I have to wait.
집 - home | 가다 - go | 기다리다 - to wait

....

4. I must wear warm clothes in winter.
겨울 - winter | 따뜻하다 - warm | 입다 - wear

....

5. I was busy, so I had to eat quickly.
*바쁘다 - busy | 빨리 - quickly | 먹다 - eat

....

*Irregular Verb: Be aware that this verb conjugates irregularly.

ANSWERS: 1. 기말고사를 잘 봐야 해요.   2. 시간이 있으면 쉬어야 해요.   3. 집에 가고 싶지만 기다려야 해요.   4. 겨울에는 따뜻한 옷을 입어야 해요.   5. 바빠서 빨리 먹어야 했어요.

Please be aware that not all sentences have one exact translation, so answers may vary slightly.

어휘

아침형 인간이에요? 저녁형 인간이에요?
[a-chim-hyeong in-ga-ni-e-yo? cheo-nyeok-hyeong in-ga-ni-e-yo?]

Recommended Vocabulary

아침형 인간은 어떤 사람이에요? [What are morning people like?]

아침 - morning; breakfast

운동을 하다 - to exercise

일어나다 - wake up; get up

일찍 - early

명상을 하다 - to meditate

계획을 세우다 - to make a plan

오전 - a.m.; the morning

할 일 - things to do

활동적이다 - active; energetic

저녁형 인간은 어떤 사람이에요? [What are night owls like?]

밤 - night

일을 하다 - to work

올빼미족 - a night owl

밤 늦게 - late at night

저녁 - evening; dinner

취미 생활을 하다 - to do one's hobbies

오후 - p.m.; the afternoon

늦다 - to be late

부지런하다 - to be diligent

아침형 인간이에요? 저녁형 인간이에요? [Are you a morning person or a night person?]

아침형 인간 - a morning person

휴일 - a rest day; a day off

잠을 자다 - to sleep; to go to bed

가깝다 - to be close

서녁형 인간 - a night/evening person

주말 - weekend

늦잠을 자다 - to sleep in; to oversleep

잠이 오다 - to fall asleep

집중력이 좋다 - to concentrate/focus well

자연스럽게 - naturally

평소 - normally; weekdays

원래 - originally/always

습관을 바꾸고 싶어요? [Do you want to change your habits?]

건강하다 - to be healthy

게으름뱅이 - a lazybones

바꾸다 - to change; switch

습관을 고치다 - to fix a habit

졸리다 - to feel sleepy

성공하다 - to succeed

행복하다 - to be happy

기분이 좋다 - to feel good

생산적이다 - productive

힘이 나다 - to gain energy

좋다 - to be good; likeable

나쁘다 - to be bad

육하원칙

아침형 인간이에요? 저녁형 인간이에요?
[a-chim-hyeong in-ga-ni-e-yo? cheo-nyeok-hyeong in-ga-ni-e-yo?]

Developing Your Answer

아침형 인간은 어떤 사람이에요?	[What are morning people like?]
아침 일찍 일어나는 사람이에요.	[They are people who get up early in the morning.]
아침형 인간은 보통 일찍 자는 편이에요.	[They are usually people who go to bed early.]
아침에 더 활동적인 편이에요.	[They're more active and in the morning.]
아침에 운동을 하거나 명상을 해요.	[They exercise or meditate in the morning.]
아침 일찍 하루 계획을 세워요.	[They plan their day early in the morning.]

Your Turn:

저녁형 인간은 어떤 사람이에요?	[What are night owls like?]
밤 늦게 잠을 자는 편이에요.	[They go to bed very late at night.]
오후에 집중력이 좋은 사람이에요.	[They tend to focus well in the afternoon.]
아침에 늦잠을 자는 걸 좋아해요.	[In the morning they like to sleep in.]
밤 늦게 일하거나 취미 생활을 해요.	[They work or do their hobbies late at night.]
저녁에 힘이 나는 편이에요.	[They tend to get energy in the evening.]

Your Turn:

육하원칙

아침형 인간이에요? 저녁형 인간이에요?
[a-chim-hyeong in-ga-ni-e-yo? cheo-nyeok-hyeong in-ga-ni-e-yo?]

Developing Your Answer

아침형 인간이에요? 저녁형 인간이에요?	[Are you a morning person or a night person?]
저는 저녁형 인간에 더 가까운 것 같아요.	[I think I'm more of a night person.]
저는 아침형 인간에 더 가까워요.	[I'm more of a morning person.]
휴일에도 오전 5 시면 자연스럽게 일어나요.	[Even on off days I get up naturally at 5 a.m.]
일찍 자려고 해도 잠이 잘 안 와요.	[Even if I try to go to bed early, I can't fall asleep.]
평소엔 일찍 일어나지만 주말엔 늦잠자요.	[I get up early on weekdays, but on weekends I sleep in.]

Your Turn:

습관을 바꾸고 싶어요?	[Do you want to change your habits?]
친구들은 다 저녁형 인간이에요.	[My friends are all evening people.]
네, 아침형 인간은 더 건강한 것 같아요.	[Yes, I think morning people are healthier.]
일찍 일어나면 더 생산적일 것 같아요.	[If I get up early I think I'll be more productive.]
늦게 일어날 때마다 게으름뱅이가 된 것 같아요.	[Whenever I get up late I feel like a lazybones.]
아니요, 저녁에 더 집중이 잘 돼요.	[No, I focus better in the evening.]

Your Turn:

쓰기

아침형 인간이에요? 저녁형 인간이에요?

[a-chim-hyeong in-ga-ni-e-yo? cheo-nyeok-hyeong in-ga-ni-e-yo?]

Try Writing Your Own Answer

1) Write your own answer below to the question   -- 아침형 인간이에요? 저녁형 인간이에요? --

2) Get your answer corrected and rewrite your corrected answer here:

You can post your writing on an app/website like *Hellotalk* or *Hinative* for free corrections.

대화

아침형 인간이에요? 저녁형 인간이에요?
[a-chim-hyeong in-ga-ni-e-yo? cheo-nyeok-hyeong in-ga-ni-e-yo?]

Example Conversation

하은: 지훈 오빠, 오빠는 아침형 인간이에요?
Are you a morning person, Jihoon?

지훈: 절대 아니에요. 하하 평소에 10시, 11시에 일어나고 새벽 1시나 2시에 자요.
Definitely not. Haha. I usually get up at 10 or 11 o'clock and I go to bed at 1 or 2 o'clock.

하은: 정말요? 그럼 오빠는 야행성 인간 인가 봐요. 저랑은 완전 반대예요. 하하
Really? Then it sounds like you're a night owl. I'm the complete opposite. Haha.

지훈: 아 하은씨는 아침형 인간이구나. 하하
So you're a morning person then, Ha-eun. Haha.

하은: 네. 할 일을 다 하려면 적어도 오전 5시 반에는 일어**나야 돼요.**
Yes. If I'm going to get everything done, then I have to get up by at least 5:30 am.

지훈: 오전 5시 반이요!? 도대체 새벽 5시반에 뭘 하는 거예요?
5:30 am!? What on earth are you even doing at 5:30 in the morning?

하은: 아침에 일어나자마자 조깅하고 아침식사도 만들고 이메일도 확인**해야 돼요.**
Right after I get up I have to jog, make breakfast, and also check my emails.

지훈: 와, 부지런하네요. 하하
Wow, you're so diligent. Haha.

문화

아침형 인간이에요? 저녁형 인간이에요?
[a-chim-hyeong in-ga-ni-e-yo? cheo-nyeok-hyeong in-ga-ni-e-yo?]

Culture Note

야행성

야행성 (literally meaning "nocturnal") is a way to describe people who tend to be more of a "night owl" (올빼미족).

Korean people used to get up relatively early, due to a government-enforced curfew which prohibited people from being out past 4am. This curfew was lifted in 1982, and since then, Korean people have started staying up later. [32] This is in part due to long work/study hours and readily available late-night entertainment, including karaoke [노래방], bars, clubs, and late-night restaurants and cafes.

Transport is also cheap and readily available, even late at night, and Korean streets are considered to be relatively safe. [33] Large Korean cities have a vibrant night-life to enjoy, with popular streets often staying busy past midnight.

Thank you!

If you have time, **please review** our book on our website or on Amazon.
Your feedback means a lot to us!
And your review helps other Korean learners out there decide
if this book is a good fit for them.
감사합니다!

From Gooseapple Books

어휘 | Vocab List

(1시간) 동안 - for (1 hour)
(강아지) 두 마리 - two (dogs)
(고양이) 한 마리 - one (cat)
(독감)에 걸리다 - to catch the (flu)
(애완동물)을 키우다 - to have/keep/raise (a pet)
(야채)볶음 - (veggie) stir-fry
(음식을) 나눠 먹다 - to share (food)
(장염)에 걸리다 - to have a (stomach bug)
(집)을 빌리다 - to rent a (house)
(폐렴)에 걸리다 - to catch/get (pneumonia)
10살 - 10 years old
1박 2일 - 2 days & 1 night
1박 2일의 여행 - a trip for 2 days and 1 night
2년 - 2 years
2주 동안 - for 2 weeks
4일 정도 - about 4 days
5년 동안 - for 5 years
X~에 따라 다르다 - it depends on X

ㄱ

가게 - a store
가깝다 - to be close
가끔 - sometimes
가능하다 - to be possible
가르치다 - to teach
가볍다 - to be light
가사 - lyrics
가수 - a singer
가을 - autumn; fall

가입하다 - to join
가족 - family
가족 여행 - a family trip
가지 - eggplant
간헐적 단식 - intermittent fasting
간호사 - a nurse
감염되다 - to have an infection
감정이입을 하다 - to empathize
갔다오다 - to go and come back
강 - a river
강남 - Gangnam
강아지 - a dog/puppy
같이/함께 - together
개 - a dog
개인 위생이 나쁘다 - to have bad personal hygiene
개인적인 공간 - personal space
거만하다 - to be arrogant
거실 - living room
거울 - a mirror
거의 (+ negative) - rarely
거의 안 (하다) - rarely (do it)
거짓말을 하다 - to lie
걱정되다 - to be worried (about)
건강 - health
건강에 좋다 - to be good for one's health
건강을 유지하다 - to stay in shape
건강하다 - to be healthy
건강해지다 - to get healthy
건조하다 - to be dry
걸레질을 하다 - to mop the floor

게으름뱅이 - a lazybones

게임을 하다 - to play games

겨울 - winter

견디다 - to tolerate

결혼하다 - to get married

경복궁 - Gyeongbok Palace

경찰서 - a police station

경험이 많다 - to be experienced

경험이 없다 - to be inexperienced

경험하다 - to experience

계획을 세우다 - to make a plan

고객 - a customer/client

고기 - meat

고등학교 - a high school

고등학생 - a high school student

고민이 있다 - to have concerns/worries

고수 · cilantro/coriander

고약하다 - a disgusting (smell)

고양이 - a cat

고양이 장난감 - a cat toy

고양이 카페 - a cat cafe

골절 - a bone fracture

공부하다 - to study

공원 - a park

공포 영화 - a horror movie

공항 - an airport

과일 - fruits

과자 - snacks

관광여행 - a sightseeing trip

관광지 - sights; attractions

관심이 있다/없다 - to be interested/not inter-

ested in

구경하다 - to view/spectate

국내 여행 - a domestic trip

국립공원 - a national park

굴 - oysters

굽다 - to bake (something)

굿즈 - merch/merchandise

귀엽다 - to be cute

귀찮다 - to be a hassle/pain

규칙적으로 - regularly

그냥 - just; only; simply

그릇 - bowls/plates/dishes

그림을 그리다 - to draw

근육 운동 - muscle building

근육을 키우다 - to build muscle

글씨 쓰기 - handwriting

금손 - to be gifted/talented at

기념품 - a souvenir

기말고사 - final exam

기분이 좋다 - to feel good

기타 - a guitar

기회가 생기다 - to have the chance

길거리 음식 - street food

깁스를 하다 - to get a cast

까탈스럽다 - to be fussy

깔끔하다 - to be neat/clean

깜짝파티 - a surprise party

깨우다 - to wake sbdy up

꼬리를 흔들다 - to wag a tail

끄다 - to turn sth off

Vocab List

ㄴ

늦잠을 자다 - to sleep in; to oversleep

나빠지다 - to worsen
나쁘다 - to be bad
나아지다 - to get better
낚시를 하다 - to fish
날씨 - the weather
날씬하다 - to be slender; slim
남자친구 - a boyfriend
남편 - husband
낮잠을 자다- to take a nap
내년 - next year
내성적이다 - to be introverted
냄새 - a smell
냄새가 나다 - to smell/stink
노래하는 법 - how to sing
녹차 - green tea
놀다 - to play; hang out
놀이공원 - a theme park
뇌진탕 - a concussion
누나 - older sister [M]
눈물이 나다 - to tear up
눈사람 - a snowman
눈이 오다 - to snow
뉴스 - the news
느긋하다 - to be easy-going
느끼하다 - to be greasy
느리다 - to be slow
능력이 없다 - to be incapable
능력이 있다 - to be capable
늦다 - to be late

ㄷ

다니다 - to attend
다른 나라 - other country
다른 사람 - another person; someone else
다시 - again
다이어트를 하다 - to diet
다정하다 - to be affectionate
닦다 - to wipe
단체 여행 - a group trip
단풍 - the fall colors
달리기 - running
담배를 피다 - to smoke
답답하다 - to be to be frustrating/suffocating/ stuffy
당일치기 여행 - a day trip
대걸레로 닦다 - to mop
대신 - instead of; rather
대학교 - a college/university
대학생 - a college student
댄스 - dance
더럽다 - to be dirty
덥다 - to be hot
데이팅 앱 - a dating app
도시 - a city
독립적이다 - to be independent
독서 - reading (hobby)
독서하다 - to read (hobby)
독학 - self-study

돈을 모으다 - to save money
동갑이다 - to be the same age
동네 - a neighborhood
동료 - a colleague/coworker
동물원 - a zoo
동생 - a younger sibling
동아리 - a school club
두렵다 - to be afraid (of)
두리안 - durian
두부 - tofu
둘 다 - both (of them)
뒹굴거리다 - to laze; to lay around; be a couch potato
든든하다 - to be reliable
듣다 - to listen; to hear
등산 - hiking
등산로 - a hiking trail
등산하다 - to hike
따뜻하다 - to be warm
따뜻한 옷 - warm clothes
따라하다 - to follow
땡기다 - to crave
똑똑하다 - to be smart
똥손 - terrible at
뛰어놀다 - to romp/frolic
뛰어오르다 - to run/jump up

ㄹ

라마단 - Ramadan
라이브 음악 - live music

락 / 록 - rock music
랩 - rap
런닝머신 - a treadmill
러닝을 하다 - to go running
레게 - reggae
레시피 - a recipe
로파이 - lo-fi
룸메이트 - a roommate

ㅁ

마시다 - to drink
마음이 편하다 - to be relaxing
마지막 부분 - the end
만나다 - to meet
만들다 - to make
만화책 - comics/manga
맑다 - to be sunny/clear
맛 - a taste
맛없다 - to taste bad
맛있다 - to be delicious
맛집 - a popular restaurant
망치다 - to ruin; to mess up
매년 - every year
매력이 있다 -to be charming
매력적이다 - charming/attractive
매일 - every day
맵다 - to be spicy
맹장이 터지다 - one's appendix bursts
머리가 길다 - have long hair
머리가 짧다 - have short hair

머물다 - to stay (temporarily)

머핀 - a muffin

먹어 보다 - to try (eating)

먹이를 주다 - to feed

먼저 - first

멋지다 - to be cool/stylish

멜로 영화 - a romance movie

면접 - a job interview

멸치 - anchovies

명상 - meditation

명상을 하다 - to meditate

명절 - a national holiday

몇 년 - a few years

몇 년 전 - a few years ago

몇 달 전 - a few months ago

몇 일 - a few days

몇 주 - a few weeks

몇 주 전 - a few weeks ago

모르는 사람 - a person I don't know

모습 - form; image

모임 - a meeting/gathering

목욕을 하다 - to take a bath

목표를 세우다 - to set goals

몸매 - one's body/figure

몸매가 좋다 - to be fit

몸을 만들다 - to bulk up

못 하다 - unable to do

무례하다 - to be rude/impolite

무섭다 - to be scary

문신이 있다 - to have tattoos

문제 - a problem/issue

문화 - culture

물렁물렁하다 - to be mushy

물어뜯다 - to chew/gnaw on

물을 주다 - to give water; to water sth (e.g. a plant)

물컹하다 - to be squishy

미래 - the future

미리 재료를 준비하다 - to meal prep

미소 - a smile

미술관 - an art gallery

ㅂ

바 - a bar

바꾸다 - to change; switch

바다 - the ocean; the beach

바닥 - the floor

바닥을 쓸다 - to sweep

바람이 불다 - to be windy; breezy

바비큐 파티를 열다 - to have a barbeque

바쁘다 - to be busy

바텐더 - a bartender

박물관- a museum

밖 - outside

밖에 가다 - to go outside

반갑다 - to greet

발라드 - ballads

발렌타인 데이 - Valentine's Day

발표 - a presentation

밤 - night

밤 늦게 - late at night

밤을 보내다 - to spend a night

밥 - 1) a meal 2) white rice

방 - room

방문하다 - to visit

방학 - a school vacation

배고프다 - to be hungry

배낭여행 - a backpacking trip

배달 음식 - delivery food

배달시켜 먹다 - to eat take out

배우 - an actor

배우다 - to learn

밴드 - a band

뱉다 - to spit out

버섯 - mushrooms

벚꽃 - cherry blossoms

베이킹을 하다 - to do baking

별로 (+ negative) - not really

병원 - a hospital

보내다 - 1) to send; 2) to spend (time)

보조개가 있다 - to have dimples

보통 - usually; normally

복근 운동 - ab exercises

봄 - spring

부모님 - parents

부산 - Busan

부엌 - kitchen

부지런하다 - to be diligent

부처님 오신 날 - Buddha's Birthday

부활절 - Easter

불가능하다 - to be impossible

불꽃놀이를 구경하다 - to watch fireworks

붐비다 - to be crowded

브로콜리 - broccoli

블루 치즈 - blue cheese

블루스 - blues

비가 많이 오다 - to rain a lot

비가 오다 - to rain

비누 맛 - a soapy taste

비린내 - a fishy smell

비싸다 - to be expensive

비싸지 않다 - to not be expensive

비타민 - vitamins

비트 - beets

빨래 - the laundry

빨래를 개다 - to fold laundry

빨래하다 - to do laundry

빵 - bread

빼다 - to remove; get rid of

뼈가 부러지다 - to break a bone

뿌듯하다 - to be proud/accomplished

ㅅ

사고가 나다 - to have an accident

사과 수확 - apple picking

사교적이다 - to be extroverted

사귀다 - 1) to date/go out; 2) get along with (friends)

사다 - to buy

사용하다 - to use

사우나 - a sauna

사이클을 타다 - to do cycling

어휘 | Vocab List

사진을 찍다 - to take pictures
사촌 - a cousin
산 - a mountain
산책 - a walk; a stroll
산책시키다 - to walk (a pet)
산책하다 - to go for a walk
살다 - to live
살을 빼다 - to reduce weight
살이 빠지다 - to lose weight
살이 찌다 - to gain weight
상처를 꿰매다 - to stitch a wound
새로운 것 - something new
새로운 곳 - a new place
새벽 - dawn
새해 - New Years Day
샌드위치 - a sandwich
샐러드 - salad
생산적이다 - productive
생일 - birthday
생일 파티 - a birthday party
샤워하다 - to shower
서양 음식 - western food
서울 - Seoul
서투르다 - to be clumsy; unskilled
선물을 교환하다 - to exchange gifts
선물을 받다 - to get/receive a present/gift
선생님 - a teacher
선호하다 - to prefer
설거지를 하다 - to do dishes
설날- Seollal (Lunar New Year's Day)
설악산 - Mt. Seorak

설탕 - sugar
성격 - personality
성공하다 - to succeed
성취감을 느끼다 - to feel a sense of accomplishment
세수하다 - to wash one's face
세탁기 - a washing machine
소개팅 - a blind date
소금 - salt
소풍을 가다 - to picnic
속 쓰리다 - to get heartburn
속이 거북하다 - to be bloated
속이 뒤틀리다 - one's stomach turns/churns
속이 울렁거리다 - to be nauseous
손님 - a guest/customer
손으로 - by hand
솔직하다 - to be honest; open
송별 파티 - a farewell party
쇼핑하다 - to shop
수박 - a watermelon
수술을 하다 - to do surgery
수업에 따라잡다 - to keep up in a class
수영 - swimming
수영장 - a swimming pool
수영하는 법 - how to swim
수영하다 - to swim
수집하다 - to collect
수프 - soup
수학 - math
수학여행 - a school/field trip
숙제하다 - to do homework

어휘 | Vocab List

순하다 - to be gentle
술게임 - drinking games
술자리 - a drinking party
숨다 - to hide
쉬다 - to rest/relax
쉽다 - to be easy/simple
스케이트를 타다 - to skate
스케이트장 - a skating rink
스키를 타다 - to ski
스트레스가 풀리다 - to relieve stress
스트레스를 받다 - to get stressed; to be stressed
스트레칭 - stretching
스트레칭하다 - to stretch
스포츠 - sports
스포츠를 하다 - to play sports
슬프다 - to be sad
슬픈 영화 - a sad movie
습관 - a habit
습관을 고치다 - to fix a habit
습하다 - to be humid
승무원 - a flight attendant
시간이 걸리다 - to take time
시간이 있다 - to have time
시간이 있을 때 - when I have time
시끄럽다 - to be loud/noisy
시내에 가다 - to go downtown
시원하다 - to be cool
시작하다 - to start
시장 - a market
시험에 떨어지다 - to fail a test

식감 - a food texture
식당 - a restaurant
식물을 기르다 - to grow plants
식사 - a meal
식사량 조절 - portion control
식사하다 - to have a meal
신년 파티 - New Years party
신문 - a newspaper
실력이 나쁘다 - to be unskilled at
실력이 좋다 - to be skilled at
실수하다 - to make a mistake
실패하다 - to fail
싫다 - to be bad; unlikeable
싫어하다 - to dislike; to hate
심심하다 - to be bored
심하게 - seriously; gravely
심하다 - to be serious/severe
싸다 - to be cheap
쌀쌀하다 - to be chilly
쓰다 - to be bitter
쓰다 - to use
쓰다듬다 - to pet/pat
씻다 - to wash/rinse

ㅇ

아기를 낳다 - to have a baby
아내 - wife
아는 사람 - a person I know
아르바이트 - a part-time job
아보카도 - avocado

Vocab List

아빠/아버지 - dad/father

아이 - a kid; a child

아직 - yet; still

아침 - morning; breakfast

아침 일과 - morning routine

아침형 인간 - a morning person

아파트 - apartment

아프다 - to be hurt/sick

아픈 환자 - a sick patient

악기를 연주하다 - to play an instrument

안경을 쓰다 - to wear glasses

안전하다 - to be safe

알레르기 - an allergy

알레르기가 있다 - to be allergic to

알앤비 - R&B

애교 - charm/cuteness

애완동물 - pets

애인 - a partner; a lover

액션 영화 - an action movie

야영장 - campgrounds

야외 - outdoors/outdoor

야외 영화를 보다 - to watch an outdoor movie

야채 - vegetables

약을 먹다 - to take medicine

양치질을 하다 - to brush one's teeth

얘기하다 - to talk/chat (with)

어렵다 - to be difficult/hard

어르신 - a senior citizen

어른 - an adult

어린이날 - Children's Day

어색하다 - to be awkward

어울리다 - to suit/match

언니 - older sister [F]

언어 - a language

얼마 안 됐다 - it hasn't been long

엄마/어머니 - mom/mother

에너지가 넘치다 - to be full of energy

엑스레이를 찍다 - to get an x-ray

엔지니어 - an engineer

여름 - summer

여자친구 - a girlfriend

여행을 가다 - to go on a trip

여행을 하다 - to travel

역사 - history

역사적이다 - to be historic

연도 - weightlifting

연습하다 - to practice

영문학 - English literature

영어 문법 - English grammar

영업 사원 - a sales associate

영화감상 - watching movies

영화를 보다 - to watch a movie

옆에 붙이다 - to stick next to

예쁘다 - to be pretty

오래 되다 - to be a while

오래 있다 - to stay for a long time

오랫동안 - for a long time

오빠 - older brother [F]

오이 - cucumbers

오전 - a.m.; the morning

오후 - p.m.; the afternoon

올리브 - olives

올빼미족 - a night owl

올해 - this year

외롭다 - to be lonely

외모 - one's appearance

외식하다 - to to be go out to eat

외향적이다 - extroverted

요가 - yoga

요가를 하다 - to do yoga

요리사 - a chef

요리하는 법 - how to cook

요리하다 - to cook

요새 - lately

요즘 - these days; lately

우리 집 - my house/family

우아하다 - to be graceful

우체국 - a post office

운동 - exercise

운동을 하다 - to exercise

운동장 - outdoor sport field

운전하는 법 - how to drive

운전하다 - to drive

울다 - to cry

웃기다 - to be funny

웃다 - to laugh

원격 근무하다 - to work remotely

원래 - originally/always

원푸드 - a 'one food' diet

위험하다 - to be dangerous

유명하다 - to be famous

유산소를 하다 - to do cardio

유연성을 향상시키다 - to improve one's flexibility

유연하다 - to be flexible; limber

유치원생 - a kindergartner

은행 - a bank

음료수 - a drink; a beverage

음악 축제 - a music festival

음악감상 - listening to music

음악을 틀다 - to put on music

의미 있다 - to be meaningful

의사 - a doctor

의상을 입다 - to wear a costume

이디엠 - EDM

이번 달 - this month

이번 주 - this week

이사하다 - to move (houses)

이틀 - 2 days

인기가 많다 - to be popular

인디 - indie

인터넷 - the Internet

인플루언서 - an influencer

일광욕을 하다 - to sunbathe

일기를 쓰다 - to journal

일어나다 - to wake up; get up

일을 하다 - to work

일주일 동안 - for a week

일찍 - early

일하지 않다 - to not work

입냄새가 나다 - to have bad breath

입원하다 - to be hospitalized

ㅈ

자다 - to sleep

자동차 여행 - a road trip

자상하다 - to be thoughtful/ considerate

자연스럽게 - naturally

자전거 - a bicycle

자전거를 타다 - to ride a bike

자주 - often

자취를 하다 - to move out

작년 - last year

잔디를 깎다 - to mow the lawn

잘 되다 - to turn out well

잘 모르는 사람 - a person I don't know well

잘 못 하다 - to not do well

잘 아는 사람 - a person I know well

잘 하다 - to do well

잘생기다 - to be handsome

잠을 자다 - to sleep; to go to bed

잠이 오다 - to fall asleep

장난기가 많다 - to be playful

장면 - a scene

장소 - a place

재미없다 - to be boring; not fun

재미있다 - to be fun; interesting

재즈 - jazz

저녁 - evening; dinner

저녁형 인간 - a night/evening person

저탄고지 - a low-fat diet

적당히 - in moderation

전공하다 - to major (in)

전남친 - ex boyfriend

전신운동 - full-body workout

전에 - before; in the past

전여친 - ex girlfriend

전통- tradition

전화하다 - to make a phone call; to call

절대 (+ negative) - never

점심 - noon; lunch

정리하다 - to organize/tidy

정신 건강 - mental health

제대로 - properly

제주도 - Jeju Island

조금 더 - a little bit more

조깅 - jogging

조깅하다 - to go jogging

조용하다 - to be quiet

졸다 - to doze

졸리다 - to feel sleepy

졸업식 - a graduation ceremoy

졸업하다 - to graduate

종종 - now and then

좋다 - to be good; likeable

좋아하다 - to like

주다 - to give

주로 - mainly; mostly

주말 - weekend

주사를 맞다 - get a shot/ injection

죽음 - death

준비하다 - to get ready

줄거리 - the plot; storyline

줄넘기 - a jump rope

출산준비 파티 - a baby shower
중간 부분 - the middle
중간고사 - midterm exam
중학교 - a middle school
중학생 - a middle school student
즐기다 - to enjoy
증상이 있다 - to have symptoms
지구온난화 - global warming
지난 달 - last month
지난 주 - last week
지루하다 - to be bored
지인 - an acquaintance
직접 - firsthand; in person
진찰하다 - to do an examination
진통제 - painkillers
집 - house/home
집값 - house price
집들이 - a housewarming party
집세 - rent (payment)
집안일 - house chores
집을 얻다 - to get a house
집중력이 좋다 - to concentrate/focus well
짖다 - to bark
짜증나다 - to be annoying
짝사랑 - one-sided love
쯤 - about; around; approx.
찜질방 - a Korean public spa

ㅊ

차 사고가 나다 - to have a car accident

차분하다 - to be calm
차사고 - a car accident
착하다 - to be nice/good
참다 - to tolerate/handle
책상 - a desk
처방하다 - to prescribe
처음 - the first time
처음부터 - from the start
첫 부분 - the beginning
청소기 - a vacuum cleaner
청소기를 돌리다 - to vacuum
청소하다 - to clean
체육 - physical education
체육관 - a gymnasium
체험 - an experience
초등학교 - an elementary school
초등학생 - an elementary school student
최고 - the best
최근 - recently
최악 - the worst
추석 - Chuseok (Korean mid-autumn holiday)
축제 - a festival
축하하다 - to celebrate
출근 전에 - before work
출근하다 - to go to work
출장 - a business trip
춤을 추다 - to dance
춥다 - to be cold
충분히 - enough
충성심이 좋다 - to be loyal
취미 생활을 하다 - to do one's hobbies

어휘 | Vocab List

치우다 - to put/clear away
친구 - a friend
친구를 사귀다 - to make friends
친근하다 - to be friendly
친척 - a relative
친한 친구 - close friend(s)
친해지다 - to get closer
침대 - bed
침대를 정리하다 - to make one's bed

ㅋ

카누를 타다 - to canoe
캐릭터의 감정 - the character's emotions/feelings
캠핑장 - a campsite
캠핑하다 - to camp
커피 - coffee
컨트리 - country music
컴퓨터 - a computer
컵케이크- a cupcake
케이크- a cake
케이크를 먹다 - to eat cake
케이팝 - K-pop
켜다 - to turn sth on
코미디 영화 - a comedy movie
코티지 치즈 - cottage cheese
콘서트 - a concert
콘서트장 - a concert venue
콴자 - Kwanzaa
쿠키 - a cookie

크리스마스/성탄절 - Christmas
크리스마스 파티 - a Christmas party
클래식 - classical music
키가 크다/작다 - to be tall/short
킥복싱을 하다 - to kickbox
킬로그램 - kilograms

ㅌ

타다 - to ride
탄수화물 - carbs
탈구되다 - to be dislocated
태어나다 - to be born
털 - fur
테니스를 치다 - to play tennis
텔레비전을 보다 - to watch TV
토마토 - tomatoes
토하다 - to throw up
퇴근 후에 - after work
퇴근하다 - to leave work
퇴원하다 - to be discharged
투어하다 - to tour
특별한 날 - a special day
특별한 목소리 - a unique voice
특유의 (X) - particular (X)

ㅍ

파스타 - pasta
파이 - a pie
파자마 파티 - a pajama party

266

파티를 열다 - throw a party
파티를 하다 - to party
팝송 / 팝 - pop music
팟럭 파티 - a potluck party
펑펑 울다 - to cry hard
페이스트리 - a pastry
편도염 - tonsillitis
편식하다 - to be picky
평소 - normally; weekdays
평일 - weekdays
표현 - facial expressions
표현하다 - to express
프로그래머 - a programmer
피부가 좋다 - to have good skin
피하다 - to avoid
필라테스 - Pilates
필요히다   to need

ㅎ

하누카 - Hanukkah
하루 - a/the day
하루 동안 - for a day
하루 종일 - all day
하루에 5분씩 - for 5 minutes a day
하우스 - house
하이킹 코스 - a hiking trail
학교 - a school
학생 - a student
한가하다 - to be free (not busy)
한강 - the Han River

한국 음식 - Korean food
한글날 - Hangul Day
한번 - once
한옥 마을 - a village of traditional Korean houses
할 일 - things to do
할로윈 - Halloween
할머니 - grandmother
할아버지 - grandfather
핥다 - to lick
핫초코 - hot chocolate
항상 - always
해가 길다 - the days are long
해가 뜨다 - the sun rises
해변 - the beach
해외 여행 - an overseas trip
해운대 해수욕장 - Haeundae Beach
행복하다 - to be happy
항생제 - antibiotics
헤비 메탈 - heavy metal
헤어지다 - to break up
헬스장 - a health club/gym
혀가 아프다 - one's tongue hurts
현제 - siblings
현지 음식 - local food(s)
현지 한식 - local Korean food
형 - older brother [M]
호수 - a lake
호텔 - a hotel
혼자 있다 - to be alone
혼자(서) - alone; by oneself

홀리- Holi

홍대 - Hongdae

화장실 - bathroom

확인하다 - to check

환영 파티 - a welcome party

활기차다 - to be active/lively/upbeat

활동적이다 - active; energetic

활발하다 - to be active/energetic

회계사 - an accountant

회사 - an office/company

회사원 - an office worker

훨씬 더 - a whole lot more

휴가 - a break; a vacation (time off from work)

휴양지 - a tropical resort

휴일 - a rest day; a day off

흐리다 - to be cloudy

힘들다 - to be difficult/hard/tiring

힘이 나다 - to gain energy

힙합 - hip hop

출처 | References

[1] None, W. (2022) *Gyeongbokgung, Wikipedia. Wikimedia Foundation.* Available at: https://en.wikipedia.org/wiki/Gyeongbokgung (Accessed: December 5, 2022).

[2] Andrea.d.steffen. (2022, April 1). *South Korea has almost zero food waste, here's how. Intelligent Living.* Retrieved September 19, 2022, from https://www.intelligentliving.co/south-korea-zero-food-waste/

[3] Soles, T. W. (2022, January 20). *6 hiking trails to try on your adventure in South Korea. World Nomads.* Retrieved September 19, 2022, from https://www.worldnomads.com/explore/eastern-asia/south-korea/top-hiking-trails-for-an-adventure-in-south-korea

[4] Sharif, H. (2018, November 26). Suneung: The day silence falls over South Korea. BBC News. Retrieved September 19, 2022, from https://www.bbc.com/news/world-asia-46181240

[5] Zeeck, M. (2022, June 9). *Guide to Health Insurance and healthcare system in South Korea: Internations go. InterNations.* Retrieved September 19, 2022, from https://www.internations.org/south-korea-expats/guide/healthcare

[6] Young, J. Y. (2022, June 17). *BTS ponders its future, and South Korea's economy warily takes note. The New York Times.* Retrieved September 19, 2022, from https://www.nytimes.com/2022/06/17/world/asia/bts-hiatus-economy-kpop.html

[7] Statista, n/a. (2022, August 16). *K-pop popularity worldwide 2021. Statista.* Retrieved September 19, 2022, from https://www.statista.com/statistics/937232/south-korea-kpop-popularity-worldwide/

[8] Jeon, S.-C. (2018, December 21). *Foreign workers in the Korean labour market: current status and policy issues. Korea, Republic of (South Korea); The Bank of Korea.*

[9] Statista Research Department. (2022). *Topic: Film industry in South Korea. Statista.* Retrieved September 19, 2022, from https://www.statista.com/topics/5587/film-industry-in-south-korea/ Korea, E. G. (2022, April 9).

출처 | References

[10] Korean Meteorological Association (n.d.). *Climate - Climate of Korea. Climate monitoring & climate.* Retrieved December 13, 2022, from https://web.kma.go.kr/eng/biz/climate_01.jsp#:~:text=The%20annual%20precipitation%20ranges%20from,about%20a%20month%20in%20summer.

[11] Weather & Climate. (n.d.). *Climate and average weather in South Korea. World Weather & Climate Information.* Retrieved December 13, 2022, from https://weather-and-climate.com/average-monthly-Rainfall-Temperature-Sunshine-in-South-Korea

[12] SPC Magazine. (n.d.). 자동등록방지를 위해 보안절차를 거치고 있습니다. *spcmagazine.com.* Retrieved December 13, 2022, from https://www.spcmagazine.com/the-story-of-bread-in-korea_happy4_210309_eng/?ckattempt=1

[13] Stern, G. (2022, November 8). *Paris Baguette, owned by the Korean-based SPC Group, expanding rapidly in the U.S. Forbes.* Retrieved December 13, 2022, from https://www.forbes.com/sites/garystern/2022/05/05/paris-baguette-owned-by-the-korean-based-spc-group-expanding-rapidly-in-the-us/?sh=1aa63336da20

[14] Elizabeth, E. (2022, June 22). *11 traditional Korean breakfast dishes. Restaurant Clicks.* Retrieved December 13, 2022, from https://restaurantclicks.com/korean-breakfast-food/

[15] Shields, S. L. (2019, December 31). *Studying Jeju Island's endangered language. The Korean Times.* Retrieved December 13, 2022, from http://www.koreatimes.co.kr/www/nation/2020/12/177_280951.html

[16] Kim, K., & Kim, K. (2022, November 21). *The haenyeo and the sea: Diving as community-led resistance. YES! Magazine.* Retrieved December 13, 2022, from https://www.yesmagazine.org/issue/bodies/2022/11/21/the-haenyeo-and-the-sea-diving-as-community-led-resistance

[17] Dunbar, J. (2020, February 18). *What foreign patients should know about being admitted to Korean hospitals. The Korea Times.* Retrieved December 13, 2022, from https://www.koreatimes.co.kr/www/nation/2020/02/177_283368.html

출처 | References

[18] World Population Review. (n.d.). *Best Healthcare in the World 2022. Best healthcare in the world 2022.* Retrieved December 13, 2022, from https://worldpopulationreview.com/country-rankings/best-healthcare-in-the-world

[19] Williams, C. (2017, February 21). *'ganbyeong'- big part of Korean Hospital Culture. KBR.* Retrieved December 13, 2022, from http://www.koreabiomed.com/news/articleView.html?idxno=160

[20] Kirkpatrick, K. (2019, September 13). *Why the Diet loved by Korean pop stars is a hit worldwide. TODAY.com.* Retrieved December 13, 2022, from https://www.today.com/health/why-k-pop-diet-korean-food-popular-worldwide-t162564

[21] The Economist Newspaper. (n.d.). *South Korea's hiking culture reflects its social pressures. The Economist.* Retrieved December 13, 2022, from https://www.economist.com/christmas-specials/2020/12/16/south-koreas-hiking-culture-reflects-its-social-pressures

[22] Kalbi. (2020, October 17). *Korean dating culture – how to find your MR or miss right in South Korea? Korean Culture Blog.* Retrieved December 13, 2022, from https://koreancultureblog.com/2015/04/30/korean-dating-culture-how-to-find-your-mr-or-miss-right-in-south-korea/

[23] Yim, H. (1966, January 1). *Summer vacation in South Korea. Creatrip.* Retrieved December 13, 2022, from https://www.creatrip.com/en/blog/4239/Summer-Vacation-in-South-Korea

[24] Kfridaynet. (2021, May 3). *How fans host a K-pop birthday cafe. Kfriday.* Retrieved December 13, 2022, from https://www.kfriday.net/post/how-fans-host-a-k-pop-birthday-cafe

[25] Petras, G. (2019, December 16). *South Koreans eat more than 1 million dogs each year - but that's slowly changing. here's why. USA Today.* Retrieved December 13, 2022, from https://www.usatoday.com/in-depth/news/2019/02/25/south-koreans-eat-more-than-2-million-dogs-every-year-but-thats-changing/2930025002/

[26] Sylvester, P. (2022, January 20). *South Korean food myths. World Nomads*. Retrieved December 13, 2022, from https://www.worldnomads.com/explore/eastern-asia/south-korea/south-korean-food-myths

[27] Park, S. S. (2018, October 5). *Vegetable rage hits South Korea as Cucumber Haters Revolt. KOREA EXPOSE*. Retrieved December 13, 2022, from https://koreaexpose.com/vegetable-rage-cucumber-haters/

[28] Parker, A. (n.d.). *20 Things You'll Only Understand If You Hate Cucumber. Urban List*. Retrieved December 13, 2022, from https://www.theurbanlist.com/a-list/20-things-youll-only-understand-if-you-hate-cucumber

[29] 오이를 싫어하는 사람들의 모임. *Facebook*. (n.d.). Retrieved December 13, 2022, from https://www.facebook.com/cucumberhaters/

[30] Yonhap. (2021, March 30). *Over half of single S. Koreans in 30s living with parents: Report. The Korea Herald*. Retrieved December 13, 2022, from https://www.koreaherald.com/view.php?ud=20210330000842#:~:text=A%20total%20of%2054.8%20percent,the%20report%20by%20Statistics%20Korea.

[31] Na, E. (2021, May 30). *Meet South Korea's 'kangaroo tribe': Ages 30 through 40 who still living with their parents. NBCNews.com*. Retrieved December 13, 2022, from https://www.nbcnews.com/news/world/meet-south-korea-s-kangaroo-tribe-ages-30-through-40-n1268724

[32] Park , M.-jong. (2015, August 13). *Morning lark or night owl? The Korea Times*. Retrieved December 13, 2022, from https://www.koreatimes.co.kr/www/opinion/2018/01/636_184791.html

[33] Sylvester, P. (2020, August 13). Is South Korea safe? what you need to know. World Nomads. Retrieved December 13, 2022, from https://www.worldnomads.com/travel-safety/eastern-asia/south-korea/is-south-korea-safe

[34] KH디지털2. (2017, January 9). 83 percent of five-year-olds in Korea go to Hagwon. The Korea Herald. Retrieved December 14, 2022, from https://m.koreaherald.com/amp/view.php?ud=20170109000747

[35] Kim, Y. (1968, January 1). Hagwons and Korea's obsession with education. Creatrip. Retrieved December 14, 2022, from https://www.creatrip.com/en/blog/9064

[36] 네이버 데이터랩 : 검색어트렌드. 검색어트렌드 : 네이버 데이터랩. (n.d.). Retrieved December 14, 2022, from https://datalab.naver.com/keyword/trendResult.naver?hashKey=N_e5f8cdda8e0b-b63a8d5e37529b1f5d97

[37] Youth employment and education in Korea | Investing in Youth: Korea | OECD iLibrary. (n.d.). Retrieved December 14, 2022, from https://www.oecd-ilibrary.org/sites/63797b4a-en/index.html?itemId=%2Fcontent%2Fcomponent%2F63797b4a-en

[38] Yonhap. (2021, December 8). Seoul's average apartment price jumps twofold under Moon Govt.: Civic Group. The Korea Herald. Retrieved December 14, 2022, from https://www.koreaherald.com/view.php?ud=20211208000673